IT'S ANOTHER WORLD

IT'S ANOTHER WORLD

Leslie Scrase

The Book Guild Ltd
Sussex, England

First published in Great Britain in 2004 by
The Book Guild Ltd,
25 High Street,
Lewes, East Sussex
BN7 2LU

Typesetting in Baskerville by
IML Typographers, Birkenhead, Merseyside

Printed in Great Britain by
Antony Rowe Ltd, Chippenham, Wiltshire

A catalogue record for this book is available from
The British Library.

ISBN 1 85776 831 0

In a Wonderland we lie,
Dreaming as the days go by.
Dreaming as the summers die:
Ever drifting down the stream –
Lingering in the golden gleam –
Life, what is it but a dream?

Lewis Carroll

This book comes with love to Wendy and Becky, of course, but also to Alison and Alex; Christopher, Karl and Cameran; Drew, Joni, Jessica and Chris; Michael and Rebecca; Edward, Aidan and Toby; Jack, Blake, Gus and Tess; and Josie and Jasper, who live in our lane, and will find themselves in this story if they look hard enough.

I would like to express my sincere thanks to the staff of The Book Guild Ltd, to my managing editor Joanna Bentley and to my copy editor, Jonathan Ingoldby. Jonathan's diligence has saved me from many infelicities of style. I have also been grateful to take on board a number of major changes which have improved my work no end. Where I have stuck to my guns and gone my own way, I hope that he will forgive me. His work has made this a better book than it otherwise would have been and I'm deeply grateful.

CONTENTS

PREFACE AND ACKNOWLEDGEMENTS

But for Wendy, my wife, this book would never have seen the light of day. The same is true of many of my other works of fiction.

Fiction?

Ah well, as to that you must judge yourselves.

But this book also owes a great deal to Jessica, Drew, Chris and Joni – flatterers all. Just think of all the times when we have been sitting peacefully in the conservatory with me in the corner twiddling my thumbs with a happy, blank expression on my face. And then suddenly, four voices in unison have demanded, 'Leslie, tell us a story.'

I remember one such occasion when I tried to get out of it. 'I don't really know where to begin,' I said.

Now it may have been Jessica, or it may have been Drew or Chris, but I think it was Joni in that quiet, commanding voice who said, 'Begin at the beginning.'

At once my mind wandered off to the trial at the end of *Alice in Wonderland*. Well it would wouldn't it, with me sitting there in my own wonderland. The White Rabbit had to read some important verses as evidence:

'Read them,' said the King.

The White Rabbit put on his spectacles. 'Where shall I begin, please your Majesty?' he asked.

Begin at the beginning,' the King said gravely, 'and go on till you come to the end: then stop.'

I also began at the beginning. That was easy enough. Stopping was not so easy because there was often a voice demanding more. And there was more: so much more. But thanks to Wendy and Jessica and Drew and Chris and Joni, I have managed to go on until I have come to the end.

But is this book for children or for adults? Is there a difference? Isn't there something of Peter Pan in all of us? One of the saddest statements in the Bible comes from Paul: 'When I became a man I gave up childish things.' This book is for adults who have not lost their sense of wonder and fantasy; for adults who can still dream dreams; for adults who have not lost the ability to be the children they once were. If there is a good deal in the book which children can enjoy too, so much the better.

One day Jessica, Drew, Chris and Joni will look back and perhaps remember. I'd like to think that when that day comes, they will pick up this book as adults and find that there is a great deal more in it than they ever knew. But not as much as you'll find in *Alice in Wonderland* of course.

Leslie Scrase

It's Another World

When we moved from suburban Surrey to rural West Dorset we didn't know that we were moving to another world.

We might never have known. If we'd left things just as they were I'm sure we would never have known. But the thing that really seemed to get things going was the planting of the rowan tree in the front garden. I'd no sooner planted it than Wendy said she'd have preferred it in the back garden. But it wasn't that. Apparently, planting that rowan upset old Maud down the lane. How was I to know? I didn't even know there was an old Maud down the lane.

But there are other people here besides old Maud: little people, big people, they appear unannounced and have an incredible impact on our lives. I wouldn't have believed it.

I never had that trouble in Surrey. But then, you wouldn't would you. All those creatures ... No. I mustn't call them 'creatures'. It's what they call 'politically incorrect' nowadays. In my day it was just plain insensitive. So I mustn't call them creatures. They are all 'people'. All those people have been extinct in Surrey for centuries. There are just too many humans there with all their clatter and noise. These people don't like clatter and noise. They don't like it at all. So Surrey is not for them – at least, not the parts of Surrey where I've lived. No, these people are long gone from Surrey. So how was I to know that they are all very much alive in West Dorset? It's another world. It really is.

And yet I'm not so sure. I think perhaps my trouble started long ago when Wendy and I got together. Oh I knew about

Peter Pan all right. And I knew that Wendy was magical. I don't suppose I'd have married her if I hadn't felt that. But Peter Pan doesn't come into it, and it was a long time before I could persuade even my magical Wendy that there are strange goings on around here. Even now I don't think she's quite sure, though she does seem to be more of a believer when she's down by the pond. Don't ask me why.

Becky knew of course, right from the start. Becky is our dog. I can hear her now as I write. She's squawking and twitching and jumping in the other room, deep in her dreams. Yes, it's the middle of the night, the safest time for writing about these things I always think. I expect she's dreaming about them now.

They didn't surprise *her*. Not ever. She knew you see. But I didn't. Not until I planted that rowan tree by the front gate. Yet even that is not quite true. There were some odd little things that happened well before that, but they were all pleasant. It was after I planted the rowan that all my troubles started.

The Day we Moved in

Even the day we moved in it was strange the way things happened. We didn't think about it at the time, except that we were amazed at how easy it all was. Not that the driver of the great removal van thought it was easy. He had to back his van all the way down the lane. It sounded so funny. There was this huge van and all the time it was going backwards a lady's voice kept saying, 'Be careful! I'm reversing. Be careful! I'm reversing.' Her voice didn't seem to fit the van at all. Back he came with both sides of the van rubbing against both hedges of the lane all the way. It was a real tight squeeze.

And then when he got here, he couldn't open the door of his cab. He clambered across onto the passenger seat, opened the window and climbed out onto the top of our garden hedge. His mate was already out and had been helping him reverse. Now he took a ladder out of the back of the van so that the driver could get off the hedge.

And then they started to unload. First of all they unloaded the kettle and tea bags and mugs and sugar (we had brought some milk with us). We all sat and had a mug of tea. Wendy spent the rest of the day making mug after mug of tea. She nearly used a whole box of tea bags.

Have you ever moved house?

If you have, you know how it is. 'Where shall I put this bed missus? Which bedroom does this wardrobe belong to? Where do you want your mower sir?' The questions go on and on.

Only they didn't.

3

There was none of that. The two men just took things off the van and brought them into the house and plonked them down. We told them not to unpack the boxes, so they just brought those in and scattered them around the house. Soon there was furniture and there were boxes in every room. The men worked really hard. I was so pleased with them that when they went I pressed a bit of paper with a picture of the queen on it into their hands. The driver climbed up the ladder onto the hedge and climbed through the window back into his cab. His mate put the ladder away and closed up the back of the van and off they went.

They had done all the work and *we* were really tired. Wendy made herself another cup of tea and me a cup of coffee, and we sat and looked at it all. We couldn't believe our eyes. I mean to say: have you ever moved house? It goes on for weeks. Sometimes it goes on for months.

'Darling?' She only calls him that when she wants something. 'Darling. I think perhaps we've got the bookcase in the wrong place.'

So all the books come out, the bookcase is moved, the books go back in.

'Darling? Now that the bookcase is over there, don't you think the piano would look rather better on this wall instead of that one?'

Pianos are murder to move but at last it is in the right place.

'I don't know ... perhaps if we put the television in *that* corner and the sofa over there and the armchairs on *this* side ...

It takes ages to get everything where her ladyship wants it all. But not in our house it didn't. We never moved a thing. Everything was just where we wanted it to be. And when we came to unpack the boxes, every box was in the right room. The kitchen boxes were in the kitchen, the dining room boxes in the dining room, the clothes boxes were in the bedrooms (even in the right bedrooms). Everything was absolutely right. It was amazing.

And yet we never guessed. It's not just Wendy who is magical. The house is magical too.

That evening we sat in the conservatory and looked out at the view with the evening sunlight shining on it. It's an incredible view. To the left a small village lies half hidden between two hills and straight ahead of us there is a small town, all orange lights at night with the shooting stars of car headlamps coming down from the hills beyond. But it was still daylight as we sat there. Beyond the town we could see for twenty miles across the rolling countryside.

It was beautifully clear that evening. We sat and sipped our drinks and gazed and gazed at the view, stupified. We have never tired of it. It is as magical as everything else here.

This really is another world you know. Somehow I must try to tell you all about it.

The Neighbours

When we first moved in, the primroses were out in the hedges down the lane and the early daffodils were out in the garden. The sun shone and went on shining for two whole months, long enough for the down to the right of us to be covered in bluebells and the woods beyond to be full of them. We felt we were in paradise and kept gasping at the wonder of it. We have never stopped.

Soon we were getting to know the neighbours a little. There aren't many. If you turn off the main road into our lane it isn't long before you come to a group of three detached houses. Ours is the third. The family who live in the first house have a cat. The two ladies who live next door to us have two black cats. If one is lucky that must mean that we are lucky twice over. They are great hunters – the cats, not the ladies. We see them out all over the place – the cats and the ladies – separately. That is, oh dear this is getting complicated. We see the cats all over the place. We also see the ladies all over the place because they are great walkers.

We come next. We are followed by a plot of land which is sometimes home to a couple of sheep. Then comes a gap. But if you walk down the lane admiring the primroses and a patch of violets on the right you will come to a smallholding on the left. When we first arrived a small man lived there with his wife. She was all round and jolly. He was always busy and active, and always very pleasant. They had two cats and some sheep and a caravan. And they had the oldest large dog I have ever met. In human years he was about a hundred and twenty. He always had a bit of a hoarse voice. He and Becky got on really well and I often used to stop and have a chat with the man – mostly about sheep prices and the weather.

There's just one more home further down the lane, right at the end of the tarmac where the lane becomes a bridle path. Actually there's one other home but we didn't know about that until much later. There's only one home you would notice. And there's a funny thing: in Surrey one of our neighbours had a plumbing business – very useful if you're clueless as I am. Yes. That's right. The man at the end of the lane has a plumbing business and he has already started to look after us. He lives with his wife and his youngest son – and two cats.

After their house the narrow lane becomes a mud bridle path for people and horses and escaped sheep and deer and foxes and badgers and mountain bikes and motor bikes and off-roaders and squirrels and rabbits and rats and mice and voles and moles and . . . you know the sort of thing, I expect.

It's very quiet and in places very dark, and it seems to go on for ever. If you walk far enough down the lane you might come across a huge feral cat. It lives without human assistance and is as large and beautiful as any cat I've ever seen. It is gorgeous, with a chocolate brown head and shoulders, a lighter brown body right back as far as its tail, and then a chocolate brown tail. It is the only cat Becky ever treats with any respect.

No that's not quite true. She likes to chase cats as long as they play fair and run away. So she was delighted to find that there were so many cats living in our lane. But if a cat is ever trapped into turning and facing Becky, then she demonstrates the wisdom of her breed. She knows full well that when it comes to cats, discretion really is the better part of valour.

And that's all the neighbours we've got in the world unless you count Joe.

Joe doesn't live on the lane. He lives in an old, old farm-house a couple of miles or so away with Barbara, his wife. And he owns all the land between his farmhouse and our lane. His dad owned the farm before him and sent him to boarding school when he was a boy. That's where Joe and I first met, so it's been good to meet up with him again.

Fairies and a Water Leaper

Once upon a time . . .

Once upon a time, soon after we arrived, Joe and Barbara came bringing a dozen eggs and a joint of beef to welcome us. Wendy made tea (and a cup of coffee for me) and then Joe and I left the women chatting while we wandered in the garden.

'I suppose you'll be digging it all up and starting again,' Joe said.

'No,' I answered. 'That's not my style. I've seen too many managers like that. They come new to a job and feel they've got to change everything just so that people know they are there. All they do is create disruption and insecurity and hostility too from all the people who liked the previous one.'

'Ah,' said Joe. He didn't say any more so I went on.

'First of all I shall wait to see just what there is. Then I shall more or less let the garden dictate what I do. It will evolve and become more "me" if you see what I mean. It isn't at all "me" at the moment but it's very beautiful. I don't want to spoil what is already here.'

The garden was beautiful. Too much heather and conifer for my liking, but very beautiful. Come to that the whole area was a picture. I've already mentioned that down the lane the hedges were full of primroses. There were lots of them growing wild in the garden too, along with masses of daffodils planted by our predecessors. And there had obviously been a huge display of snowdrops earlier in the year, but they were all over. It would be a mistake to start digging. I didn't want to disturb a thing, not yet anyway.

We stood in silence and then walked to the bottom of the garden. Joe was looking around carefully. He said, 'So you'll keep the primroses wherever they choose to grow.'

'Good heavens, yes.'

'And what about other wild flowers?'

'You mean, will I encourage them or will I root them out as weeds?'

'Yes,' he said. 'You've got a bank of herb robert over there for instance. What will you do with that?'

'I shan't touch it. It's beautiful, all of it, flowers and leaves too, and all so colourful. I'm not saying I shall never interfere with wild flowers in the garden, but I shall leave them or encourage them if I can. They're special.'

'So you'll leave that herb robert then?'

'Yes of course I will. I couldn't do anything better there if I tried.'

'Ah,' he said and paused. 'That should please the fairies I reckon.'

I looked at him. Deadpan face he had. Part of the fun of being with Joe was always that I never quite knew when to take him seriously. He's got a real poker face. He could always pull the wool over my eyes. Not surprising I suppose. I was a townie living in the country whereas he was a true countryman who knew it inside and out. So when he talked about pleasing the fairies I just said, 'Oh good,' and then I added, 'twit.'

'Don't you call me a twit. I suppose you'll be telling me you don't believe in fairies next.'

'Of course I don't.'

'Well you'd better way start. If you'm gwain to live in the country you need to know country folk and their ways. You must get to know what the fairies like and what they don't like. And one of the things they like is herb robert. 'Tis Robin Goodfellow's favourite.'

10

Joe really could be serious about the most ridiculous things.

'Oh yes,' I said. 'And who is Robin Goodfellow when he's at home?'

He looked at me full of suspicion. 'You're having me on. You mean to say you don't know Robin Goodfellow?'

'Never heard of him.'

'Good Lord. What is the world coming to? Robin's as well known as any sprite in the world and he's as mischievous as they come.'

'A sprite? Oh, another one of your fairies; a bit like Puck.'

'*Like* Puck? He *is* Puck, and herb robert is his favourite flower – a bit like an emblem you might say.'

'So as long as I leave that bank of herb robert I shall have Puck and the fairies on my side, is that what you're saying?'

'Ah. That's right.'

'That's all right then.'

We walked on round the garden and indoors, and I toddled off to the loo. When I flushed it, it rumbled something terrible, just as if I had started up an engine. As far as we could make out, it was the only fault in our new home.

'What on earth is that noise?' asked Joe in the other room.

'It's our flush,' said Wendy. 'It's pretty awful isn't it? Leslie has had a go at it but he's no plumber I'm afraid.'

'Sounds bad,' said Joe. 'I expect you've got a water leaper.'

'Oh Joe,' his wife exclaimed but his face was as straight as a die.

'What's a water leaper?' asked Wendy.

'Horrible things, water leapers. They look a bit like toads but they can swell up huge. Always causing trouble those things are.'

'Here we go again. A garden full of fairies and a water leaper in the house,' I commented. 'It's probably just something wrong with the flushing mechanism, the ballcock

11

or something,' I added knowledgeably. 'I'm sure it's something a plumber could fix in no time.'

'You need to call your neighbour from down the lane,' said Barbara. 'He'll deal with it.'

Joe sucked through his teeth. 'Gyaw,' he said, 'that'll cost ee a pretty penny. But you never know, it might work.'

Barbara laughed. 'Don't take any notice of him. Your neighbour won't overcharge you at all. He's very fair.'

So I called him in and he solved our problem without much trouble or expense and we heard no more of water leapers or fairies for a while.

And yet, unwittingly, it was our neighbour who started the ball rolling again, not indoors but out in the garden. As he was leaving after he had mended our flush, he pointed to a large flagstone lying on one of our front lawns.

'I'm surprised you don't shift that,' he said. 'It's been there for ages but it really spoils the look of that lawn.'

It did too, but it was pretty hefty. 'Easier said than done,' I thought. But I agreed with him and added, 'I'm sure I'll get round to it one day.'

The Bucket

Our neighbour was right about our front garden and his words bugged me. In our front garden there are two small lawns. At the end of one of them, slap in the middle of the grass, there was a heavy paving stone. I haven't got a crowbar but one day I managed to get an old garden fork under one end of it. I levered it up enough to shove a wedge underneath. Then I got my fingers underneath it far enough to be able to lift. I planned to heave it upright and then 'walk' it away. But that would have meant stepping forward. Luckily I discovered in time that there was nowhere to step to. Underneath the paving stone there was nothing but a deep hole.

Eventually, with a lot of heaving and shoving, I managed to get the paving stone away from the hole. It really was a deep hole – very deep indeed. It was a well, but the water was a long, long way down.

'Oh thank you! Thank you very much! You are a nice man.'

I could have sworn I heard someone, but though I looked all around I couldn't see anyone. So I went to fetch some rope (an old clothes line) and my battered old metal bucket. There's quite a story behind that bucket. I must have had it for all of twenty years. It happened like this.

A long time ago I was given the job of looking after four Irishmen for three days. They were over here from Ireland for a wedding. But they had decided to make a short holiday of their trip. On the first day I collected them from their hotel and asked them where they wanted to go.

13

'Over the bridge,' they said.

So I drove them two miles to the bridge across the river, and over we went.

'Straight on,' they said.

And that's how it was for the whole of the three days. I never knew where we were going, but they did. They were going from one pub to another. At each pub they had made arrangements for a room where they could drink (out of hours) and play cards.

We didn't start very early, so we would get to our first pub at lunchtime and then they would play and drink through the afternoon. Then on to a second pub for two or three hours in the early evening. And finally to a third for a late night session before going back to their hotel. I assisted them to their rooms and then went home myself.

After three days, which became more and more fun as the time wore on, you can imagine the sort of state they were in on the morning of the wedding. I arrived at ten-thirty just to make sure they were up. There they all were, sitting around a table playing cards, with a drink to chase the blues away. At eleven they decided to go and change into their dress suits – toppers and tails were the order of the day. Three of them managed very well. They had a shower and changed. The fourth got into a bit of a muddle. He changed and then showered, which made a bit of a mess of his suit. His friends did their best to tidy him up, by which time it was getting a bit late.

We set off for the church and then one of them exclaimed, 'Holy Mary, Mother of God! Did you see *that*?'

The others looked.

'Oh my God. Oh sweet Jesus, we've overdone it this time. Driver, can you see what we can see?'

'What's that?' I asked.

'Did you see that girl leading an elephant by the side of the road?'

14

Well of course I did. You could hardly miss seeing an elephant could you? But I wasn't letting on.

'I'm afraid I had my eyes on the road,' I said.

'Oh dear God. Hurry and get us to the church driver.'

I didn't mention the fact that the circus was in town – just got them to the church as fast as I could.

The bride was just going in, followed by her bridesmaids. My four men completed the procession. I hoped somebody diverted them into pews before they got to the front of the church.

They may have been the last in. They were certainly the first out. We drove back to their hotel, where the wedding reception was to take place. Two of them hurried in to alter all the place names at the tables. One of the others gave me fifty pounds and told me to go to the local hardware shop and buy five metal buckets.

'Five metal buckets?' I queried.

'Exactly,' he said. 'Five metal buckets.'

So I did as he said and brought the buckets back to him.

'That's one for each of us. We shall be able to make plenty of noise at the reception with those.

'But there are only four of you.'

'The fifth is for you, to remember us by.'

And I have never forgotten them.

Now, where was I? That's the trouble with getting old. The memory bank is so full that it's easy to get sidetracked. Let's see. Oh yes. I fetched a rope and my metal bucket, didn't I? Then I lowered the bucket down to the water and let it sink. It was amazing. It must have been well over thirty feet down to the water and then the water was a good six feet or more deep. I drew the bucket up to the top of the well and lifted it out. There, sitting on the rim was a water nymph and beside her was an Irish leprechaun. What a contrast. She was exquisite while he looked just like a wizened old man. He must have lived with the bucket ever since it was given to me and I never knew.

15

The nymph said, 'Thank you. Oh thank you kind sir.'

It was the voice I had heard earlier

'I've been shut up in the darkness of that dungeon for years and never seen a glimmer of light.'

The leprechaun wasn't paying much attention. He hopped off the bucket and went and fetched one of my sea shells. You didn't know about my sea shells? I must tell you about them some time. Anyway, he hopped back onto the bucket, filled the sea shell with water, sipped it and said, 'Don't think much of this whiskey. It's got no bite.'

But I wasn't listening to him. I only had eyes for my lovely water nymph.

I explained to her that I would have to close the well again for a time so that the grandchildren didn't fall in, but I promised that as soon as I could I would put a proper cap on the well with a door.

'Oh, thank you! Thank you kind sir.' Her voice had all the music of a tiny waterfall. I was so enchanted that I didn't notice that her conversation seemed to be somewhat limited. She stood on the edge of the bucket and dived back down into the well with hardly a splash. The leprechaun was still sipping the water and grumbling, 'Don't think much of this whiskey.'

I went and fetched Wendy. We brought two glasses and each had a glass of water from the bucket. It was cold and fresh and pure: it was beautiful.

'Lovely,' said Wendy.

'Lovely indeed!' said the leprechaun. 'That just shows how little she knows about whiskey.'

I didn't argue with him because Wendy hadn't noticed that he was there. Well, without a few whiskeys she wouldn't would she?

'I've decided to open up the well,' I said.

'What on earth for? Just think of the danger!'

'There won't be any danger. I'll have a locked gate over it.'

'But what's the point?'

I could hardly tell Wendy that the point was that I wanted to be able to see my lovely water nymph again could I? So I said, 'I can use the water for the garden. Just think, our own free supply.'

She wasn't very impressed but she said, 'Oh you do as you like, but you needn't think you're going to use *that* – and she pointed at the bucket. Now the leprechaun thought that she was pointing at him and he was not very pleased. While Wendy walked back to the house, I did my best to explain but he was not easily mollified.

'Here,' I said, 'give me that shell and stay right where you are.' I took the shell and hurried indoors. Luckily Wendy was not in sight. I took a bottle of Irish whiskey from the cupboard, poured a thimbleful into the shell and took it out to him. He sipped suspiciously and then his face lit up.

'Now that's what I call whiskey!' he said. I heaved the paving stone back over the well. He took another sip, 'Magnificent,' he said.

I wound up the rope and slung it over one arm and then, very carefully, I picked up the bucket with him sitting on the rim. I put the bucket back where it belonged in the shed and asked, 'Are you OK living with the bucket?'

'OK?' he said, taking another sip. 'Am I OK? You and me,' he said, taking another sip, 'you and me are friends for life. Friends for *life*.' I slipped quietly away and left him to it.

The Well

I had promised my water nymph that I would open up her well so that she was no longer a prisoner. She would be free to enjoy the light from time to time. And I hoped that sometimes I would catch a glimpse of her again. So I called the local blacksmith and arranged for him to come and measure up. On the appointed day I heaved the great slab from the top of the well in preparation for his visit.

'Oh thank you kind sir! Thank you very much.'

There she was again, standing on the well's brick surround. I was entranced. I explained about the blacksmith's visit and that I would have to close the well after he had been, until the new trapdoor was ready. She quite understood, and dived back into the water.

The blacksmith arrived. He looked every inch a blacksmith: shiny jet black hair, bushy black eyebrows, broad, broad shoulders, black-haired barrel chest and rippling muscles. You could imagine him putting champion weightlifters to shame and tearing top wrestlers apart. He was tough. No doubt about that.

'Afternoon.'

'Good afternoon. Thanks for coming.'

'Nice place you've got here.'

'Yes.'

'Where's this well then?'

There was obviously no messing about with him. Time to get down to work.

'Over here. I've taken the lid off so that you can get a proper look.'

He looked down into the well, put his hands in front of his eyes and staggered back.

'Oh my Gor,' he said. 'That's some hole that is. Can't never stand heights. Oh my. Makes me proper weak about the knees.'

It looked so funny to see that big tough man all white and trembling. He stood for a while taking great gulps of fresh air. Then he took out his measure, got on his knees and measured up all round the well, taking great care not to look down again. When he had finished he crawled a safe distance away, stood up and told me that he would take about three weeks to finish the work.

'But I reckon as I'll have to bring someone else to fit it when 'tis done. I can't look down there again.' And with that he was gone.

I turned to heave the slab back over and a voice said, 'Funny man. Fancy not being able to look down into my lovely well.'

There she was again – exquisite. I decided not to tell her that I found heights a bit difficult too. Down she dived and I hauled the stone back into place.

A few days later I was standing in the garden thinking about the well and about my collection of shells. Oh, I was going to tell you about my shells wasn't I?

We go to the beach fairly often. Well we would wouldn't we, living so close to the sea. I didn't tell you we lived close to the sea? Are you sure? Well we do. From the end of our lane you can look down over the bay, so of course we go down to the beach pretty often. And when we're there I can't resist picking up a few shells and bringing them home. I used to put them all on the window ledges but then Wendy got a bit stroppy.

'You can keep them there if you like,' she said, 'as long as you do the dusting.'

Me! Do the dusting! I wouldn't know one end of a duster from the other. I quietly took the shells out into the garden, and I must say they make quite a nice show out there. But they need a sort of something to give them a point of focus. Now I was beginning to think perhaps I had one – and that was when old Joe turned up.

'Mornin'.'

'Hello Joe.'

'What you doin' out here then?'

'I was thinking.'

'Ah. I thought you looked a bit lost.'

I ignored his sarcasm. Wendy came out with a load of washing. 'Morning Joe.'

'Mornin' missus.'

'Mug of tea?'

'Yes please.'

I pointed to the stone and told him about the well underneath. Then, as we walked indoors I told him I was planning to open it up. He sucked through his teeth.

'Asking for trouble that is.'

'I suppose you're going to start talking about water leapers again.'

He grinned. 'You going to put an electric pump to un then?'

'No,' I said, 'nor an ordinary pump either.'

'No, I don't think you would put in one of they,' he said.

'Why not?' asked Wendy. 'I think that would look rather nice.'

'Well, you see,' said Joe, 'he'll remember the first time he ever came to stay with me.'

I remembered it all right, and if the story had to be told I preferred to tell it myself.

'When we were boys, Joe used to take me home to his parents' farm to stay. They didn't have gas or electricity and they didn't have running water. It had to be drawn from the pump in the yard.'

He interrupted me. 'I gave he a jug and asked un to fill it with water. Well I niver thought as how he wouldn't know nothin' about pumps.'

20

I chipped back in again. 'I raised and lowered the pump handle the way I'd seen them do it, but nothing happened. So Joe called out, "Have a look up the spout. There must be something blocking it".'

'And while he was lookin' up, I worked the handle some more an' the water caught 'im full in the face,' Joe said gleefully. 'Gyaw, he looked such a fooyull. He didn't know nothing about pumps and pressure and such like. I wetted he that day proper, so I don't think he'll be putting a pump to his well. Not after that.'

And off he went, chortling away and leaving Wendy highly amused. As for me, well, how would you like being made to look such a fool?

Right on time the blacksmith rang me to say that the new top was ready. He came with his assistant and the two of them fitted it and left. I lifted the door and fetched my old bucket and the rope from the shed.

'Where are we going today?' asked the leprechaun.

'Back to the well,' I said, 'it's ready now.'

'Don't know that I'm very keen on that,' said the leprechaun. 'I'll have to keep hopping off every time you want to put it down to that nymph. And if you leave it there, I'll be on view to anyone.'

'You'll be all right,' I said, 'you see if you won't.'

I fixed the rope to the well-head and tied the other end to the bucket and called Wendy for the first ceremonial lowering.

'You're not putting that old bucket there.' I ought to have known she would stick to her guns.

'Well, yes, I thought it would be ideal.'

'No. Definitely not,' she said. 'We need something that looks decent. Not that battered old thing.'

'How dare she,' said the leprechaun. 'I've never been so insulted in my life.'

'Hush,' I said, 'she doesn't mean you. She's talking about the bucket.'

21

'What did you say?' Wendy thought I was talking to her. She couldn't see the leprechaun. It was all very confusing.

'I said that I rather like the bucket.'

'Well I don't. You can use it today but then you can take it down again.'

'Women!' said the leprechaun.

'Don't you speak like that.' This time it was the high, piping voice of the water nymph. She had come up to see what all the fuss was about. While the water nymph and the leprechaun were arguing with one another Joe arrived. He looked at me standing beside the well.

'Still thinkin'?'

'Hello Joe. We've opened it you see. And I'm thinking I'll put my shell collection around it. It should make quite a feature.'

'No,' said Wendy. 'That wouldn't look at all right. What we need is a pond. They'd look lovely scattered around a pond. We always used to have a pond. I'd like to have one again and I know just the place.'

'You might get a merman if you had a pond,' Joe said quietly, and then he looked down the well. 'Gyaw,' he said, 'that's some deep well. Just the place for a water leaper.'

You probably remember that a water leaper is a bit like a large toad. It can swell up like a toad too and make itself look huge.

'Water leaper,' I said contemptuously. 'Water nymph more like.' But I didn't tell him that that was what we actually had in the well or that she had dived down out of sight when he arrived.

'Water leaper. Water nymph. What does it matter. They're as bad as one another.'

'What do you mean?' asked Wendy.

'Don't you remember how the water nymphs tempted King Arthur to strip off and go swimming with them in the nuddy?'

'Like the vicar in *A Room with a View*,' she said. 'I enjoyed that.'

She did. She enjoyed that far too much for my liking. She watched it over and over, giggling away.

Grumpily I said, 'A water nymph is hardly likely to persuade anyone to go swimming in the well.'

In order to change the conversation I lowered the bucket and drew up some water. That wasn't all I drew up. My beautiful water nymph was sitting on the edge of the bucket combing her long golden hair.

'There,' said Joe pointing. 'What did I tell you? Just look at that warty old toad. You've got a water leaper there.'

But all I could see was my water nymph. Through my mind flashed words on a little ornament we had in the bathroom: 'You've got to kiss a lot of toads before you meet the handsome prince'. Well I hadn't kissed any toads but here was my beautiful princess. I could see her all right.

'There's no water leaper,' I said. 'You're imagining things.'

At that moment she leapt onto my shoulder.

'Ugh,' said Joe. 'Get'n off your shoulder. Great bloated thing. He'll give you no end of trouble.'

I glanced at my shoulder. There was my nymph. She winked and I laughed. I was enjoying this.

'What on earth's the matter with you Joe? There's no water leaper there.'

My nymph dived straight from my shoulder down the well.

''Tis gone,' said Joe with obvious relief. 'Dived down the well. Thank goodness for that. You'd better close it up quick.'

Wendy had been watching all this with a great deal of amusement. She hadn't seen anything unusual at all, so she said, 'Come off it Joe. You're a darned good actor but he's not biting. Come in and have a mug of tea.'

But Joe was looking quite shaken. 'A drop of whisky might be better,' he said.

'Whiskey? Whiskey? Did someone say whiskey?' cried my leprechaun.

'What was that?' said Joe.

'Oh it's our leprechaun,' I answered casually.

And Joe relaxed and grinned. 'Now that *is* nonsense,' he said. 'You only find leprechauns in Ireland.'

I didn't argue. I just said, 'I'd better see to your whiskey then.' And I gave him a drop of the Irish and also slipped out with a thimbleful for himself. That made sure everybody was happy.

'That was a bit of fun wasn't it?' said my nymph, back on top of the well again.

'I didn't know you could manage such things,' I said.

'Ah well,' she sighed, 'half the time we see the things we expect to see. We don't see what is really there. Goodbye for now you lovely man,' and she dived down into her well.

'That was very profound,' I said.

'She'd be a lot more profound if she drank some of this,' said the leprechaun.

I untied his bucket and took it back to the shed. 'I'm sorry Wendy won't let me keep you on the well,' I said.

He sipped his whiskey. 'Better to live here in peace,' he said, 'than to have to put up with that silly woman.'

'How dare you,' I said. 'I'll have you know. . .'

But he interrupted me. 'Not your wife. That other one from down the well, "you lovely man".' He imitated my water nymph too well for my liking. And I didn't like her being called 'silly' either. She was lovely. In a bit of a huff I left him and went back indoors.

Wendy was saying, 'You know you really shouldn't go on about those things Joe. Talk about water leapers long enough and you'll have him believing your nonsense.'

I sniffed and lifted my chin. Insulted I was. But Joe didn't answer. He just gulped down the last of his whiskey and held out his glass for a refill.

The Pond

I'm not a great one for ponds. Apart from the work, all you can do with a pond is look at it. Nor did I feel that this garden lent itself to a pond really. But if Wendy wanted one...

I walked round and round puzzling over the best place to dig. Eventually I decided on a spot in a corner of the lower lawn. But I wasn't in any hurry to start. I remembered digging out the pond in our last garden. Developers were building a new estate on the other side of our hedge when I started digging. Bulldozers set about levelling the ground and piled up huge heaps of soil. Meanwhile I was working away with a spade and a wheelbarrow, spreading the soil around the garden. Eventually the hole was complete.

Carolyne came and looked at it. She also noticed the heaps of soil piled upon the other side of the hedge. Who is Carolyne? *You don't know who Carolyne is? Everybody* knows who Carolyne is. Surely I must have told you about Richard and Andrew, Paul and Carolyne, Jean and Christine and their wives and husbands and the umpteen grandchildren? I haven't? Oh. Well they're the family and Carolyne is one of them.

She came and looked at the little hole I had dug for my pond and then she looked at the mountains of soil on the other side of the hedge and with a grin she commented, 'I wouldn't have thought that little hole would have produced so much soil!'

And now I had to begin digging a hole all over again. I thought I'd better make sure that Wendy agreed with my choice of position. And of course she didn't.

25

'No, no, no. I don't want you digging up the lawn. It would spoil that part of the garden completely. The pond must go over in that corner. That's the perfect place for it.'

'That corner' was a spot beside the bank of herb robert where the old septic tank had been before our house went onto the mains. It was covered over now with flagstones in a sort of patio. Although it was a corner that we didn't seem to be able to do anything with, and although a pond would look just right there, I didn't much fancy all the work of opening it up. Who knows what I would find underneath?

'No you silly man. I don't want you to open it all up. We can put a free-standing pond on the top.'

Now that did seem a good idea. Next to no work at all. Yes. I could go along with that. So I measured up and off we went and bought our pond and put it in the corner of the garden. And it looked just . . . completely wrong. Have you seen those large corner baths advertised? Imagine a dark green corner bath stuck up in your garden and think how you would like it.

'If you build a nice rockery all round it and blend it in with its surroundings it will look perfect,' Wendy said.

So there was work to be done after all: a lot of work.

Ages ago our hill used to be quarried for stone for building the nearby village and there is still a lot of stone lying about. Day after day I went up there with the old shopping trolley, but eventually it gave up the ghost. So then I took my rucksack and had many an uncomfortable journey. My shoulders hadn't been so sore since square-bashing with a First World War rifle in the Navy. No, I wasn't in the First World War. I wasn't even in the Second World War. And I never fired the rifle. The country couldn't afford the bullets so we just learned to march with rifles. What am I talking about rifles for? Oh yes – rocks in my rucksack. Eventually that burst. But we had a large bag made of very strong plastic, so I started taking that with me until at long last I had enough rocks to start building. It took ages.

The pond was filling up nicely, so I gave it a bit of help with bucket after bucket of water from the well and then we went out and bought a few plants. At last our pond was beginning to look as though it belonged. We felt that when we had planted the rockery as well, it should really look right. And I began to put some of my seashells down there.

Joe had been round a number of times while the work was going on. Although he had been interested, he hadn't made much comment. But when he saw me putting the seashells down, he sucked in through his teeth and said, 'I shouldn't do that if I were you.'

I decided not to ask him why, but Wendy did.

'Well you might get a merman in the pond.'

'Rubbish,' I said. 'You only get mermen in the sea.'

'I should think a merman would be rather nice,' Wendy said quietly.

'You're wrong,' said Joe. 'There's many a merman in fresh water. You just go up to Scotland and ask any of the people who live round the lochs.'

'Even if that's true, don't you think our pond is a bit small for a merman? And why just a merman anyway? Why can't we have a mermaid as well?' I laid on the sarcasm as hard as I could.

'Merman, mermaid, they're just as bad as one another. And they come in all sizes so there's no reason you shouldn't have one or two – probably hiding up in one of those shells listening to us as we speak I shouldn't wonder.'

Again Wendy murmured dreamily, 'I wouldn't mind a merman at all. Not in the least. No I wouldn't mind that at all.'

But Joe didn't hear. I said, 'What do you mean, "they're just as bad as one another"? Why do these creatures' (I used to call them that) 'always have to be bad?'

'Don't you remember the trouble Odysseus had with those mermaids?'

'Those were sirens and that was almost three thousand years ago. Don't you think you're stretching things a bit far?'

''Tisn't just the ancients who had trouble with mermaids. Sailors have always had trouble with them. You know that.'

'I know the *stories*...' I was going to go on with some really cynical talk about how all those old stories had died out, but then I thought about the leprechaun and about my lovely water nymph. So I didn't say another word. Nor did we see any sign of mermen or mermaids.

We left the pond to mature for a time and then bought a few fish. Wendy was the one who always looked after the fish. She never walked round the garden without going down to see them and to check that they looked content. And she was the one who fed them. Early each evening she went down to the pond, cast in some fish food and stood back to watch them rise to take it.

One evening when she was there, she was surprised to hear, 'Good evening beautiful lady.' She looked around but I wasn't there. 'Daft ha'porth,' she thought. 'What's he playing at?'

'Hello, lovely lady.'

She ran and looked behind the bushes. I wasn't there. She turned back to the pond and then she saw him. Gosh. He was magnificent. An Australian life-guard in miniature. He really was ... just ... wow. She took a deep breath. 'Get a grip on yourself woman,' she said to herself.

'Hello,' she said.

'You wanted a merman,' he said.

'Yes,' she said. 'But how did you know? Surely Joe wasn't right.'

He smiled.

'He *was*! You were in one of those shells. You were listening you naughty man.'

''Fraid so,' he said, 'but never mind that. Thank you for my pond.'

'It's my husband you've got to thank. He put it in.'

'Your husband! I've got nothing to thank him for. He was the one who brought me here, away from the sea. And he would just have left me if it hadn't been for you. You were the one who wanted a pond, not him.'

'Oh don't be too hard on him. He didn't know he was bringing you with the shells.'

'That's the trouble with you humans. Always meddling with things you don't know anything about. Always interfering in other creatures' lives. Always making a mess of our world.'

'I'm so sorry,' said Wendy, who was beginning to feel thoroughly ashamed of being human.

'Oh not *you*, lovely lady. Thanks to you I've got this lovely, splendid, peaceful pool all to myself and no one to spoil it – none of those silly mermaids. No. This suits me fine, and we shall be able to have a chat whenever you come down here.'

I walked down the garden to join Wendy by the pool but I was too late to hear him say, 'Whoops, look who's coming.'

Joe was with me. We both thought we saw a fish jump. Wendy could have told us that it was her merman diving into the depths of the pool.

'Seen any mermen?' asked Joe with a chuckle.

'Don't start that stuff,' I said. Neither of us noticed Wendy blushing as she stood there.

'Come and have a look at my fish,' she said.

'How many have you got?' asked Joe.

'We only put half a dozen in. We wanted to see how they would get on before we stocked the pond properly.'

'Six did you say?'

'Yes.'

'There's seven swimming in there.'

Wendy blushed again as she looked. I looked too.

'Get on with you,' I said, 'There's only six.'

'It's difficult to count with them all moving about so. But I reckon there's seven.'

'Six,' I said.

'Stop arguing,' said Wendy.

'Yes missus,' said Joe, 'but you might have got lucky you know. The chap in the shop may have picked out seven instead of six. It's easy to do with fish.'

'Six,' I said.

'Mug of tea Joe?'

'Please.'

Neither of us heard Wendy murmur, 'You don't know how lucky Joe. He's magnificent.'

Not even Wendy heard a voice whisper, 'Yes I am aren't I, and you're a bit of all right yourself lovely lady.'

Ragwort

By the time I'd seen to the well and the pond, summer was half way gone. We had some really hot days that July. There were days when everything seemed to be shimmering in a heat haze. I found that I was wearing my sunglasses more and more.

They were a good pair of sunglasses. In fact, they were the best I'd ever had. They used to belong to Wendy's mother so they were pretty old, some of the first ever made I expect. They were ideal for me, only, sometimes I wonder. Do everybody's sunglasses have the same effect? Sometimes I seem to see things differently, if you see what I mean.

Looking across a field of grass I could imagine it was a lake with the wind rippling the water. And up on the hill I could have sworn that the ragwort was flying across the hillside, zooming about in the air.

I was leaning on a gate just gazing one day when Joe came striding across the fields. He's about the same age as me but he's tall and upright and slim, and as tough as any man I've ever met. He joined me and we leaned on the gate together. There's a timelessness about the country. I never used to stop and lean anywhere. Joe looked at the ragwort in the field.

'Better not get any of that stuff in the winter feed for the cattle,' he said.

'Oh? why?' I asked.

'Poisonous. Once it finishes flowering and dries out, the cattle and the horses don't recognise it any more. If they eat it, it can kill them. Poison builds up inside them.'

31

'But that's awful.'

'Yes. A lot of farmers won't have the stuff on their land. They'd like to see it wiped out altogether. But I reckon they never look at it. I always like to have a bit of it about.'

'It is beautiful isn't it? Look at that patch over there by the hedge with the red campion. You couldn't get anything lovelier than that in a garden.'

'Beautiful!' he exclaimed. 'What's that got to do with anything? 'Tisn't because 'tis beautiful that I haves it on my land. 'Tis because its useful.'

'Useful?'

'Yes. Come and have a look – and stand quiet. Don't fidget. You townies be always on the fidget. Can't be quiet if you try.'

So I tried.

' There. D'ee see?'

'I'm not sure what I'm looking at. Do you mean the insects, the butterflies and all those caterpillars?'

'That's right. You'm learning. See they black and gold caterpillars?'

'Lovely aren't they.'

'Lovely is it? Well, they're the caterpillars of the cinnabar moth and that's a little beauty with red rear wings. Get rid of the ragwort and you get rid of the cinnabar moth. Burnet moths love it too, and soldier beetles and – well you can see for yourself. Just look at all the visitors just to that one plant. Look at all those bees and hoverflies.'

'Yes. I've often heard that getting rid of all the flowers – I suppose you farmers would call them weeds – from the fields has cut down on the insects and the birds too.'

'So it has I'm afraid. And I'm as guilty as all the rest. Look at that ragwort again. Come September when all the seeds are on it and on that patch of dashulls over there, you'll have flocks of goldfinches all over them. What are they going to do if we get rid of all these things?'

'Dashulls? oh, thistles.'

'But if ragwort is poisonous . . .'

'If it's poisonous you've got to ask yourself *how* poisonous. Read some papers and you'd think thousands and thousands of cattle and horses are killed by ragwort every year. Well, I've been farming all my life and I've always had ragwort on my land and I've never lost anything to it yet. I read two books not long ago. One of them said that it causes the deaths of "a large number of livestock annually". The other said that it is "mildly poisonous". Now which one do you believe?'

'I don't know do I?'

'No more you do. Well I don't believe either of them. When people says to me "farmer beware", I just says to myself, "farmer, take care". That's all it needs. Besides, there's the fairies to think about too.'

'Fairies?' I said with a grin. 'Here we go again.'

'Don't you mock,' Joe said seriously. 'These aren't things to laugh or joke about.'

I thought about my water nymph and my leprechaun. I had seen those hadn't I? Quite often in fact. Perhaps it was wise not to mock, just in case.

'You'm too cocky,' Joe went on. 'There are more things in heaven and earth than you dream of. Just look at that ragwort now. Do you see how 'tis all flying about over the hillside?'

Funnily enough it did *look* as if it was all flying about. I'd already noticed it. But that was just the wind and the hazy sunshine and my sunglasses.

'That's the fairies,' he said. 'They use ragwort the way witches use broomsticks. In fact, witches used to use it before they went upmarket.'

He looked so serious while he spun me this load of codswallop, but we weren't boys at school any more. He couldn't kid me. So I just said 'poof' to show that I didn't take him seriously.

And then I saw the feral cat. It was staring at me and all the hairs on the back of my neck went all tingly.

The Rowan Tree

We'd had gooseberries from bushes down the lane. The wild strawberries in our hedge and the self-sown or bird-sown raspberries by the pond were all over and done with. We had picked our season's blackberries from the hedges in the fields. We had dithered over the elderberries because I'm not keen, and we had collected damsons from some trees growing wild below the hill. We had been up on the down to a magnificent apple tree there and come back laden almost beyond belief. And Wendy had made enough jam and jelly to last a small army for twelve months or more.

I had also planted a few fruit trees of my own.

Why bother? You may well ask. I planted some apple trees and a plum. And that was also when I planted my rowan tree by the front gate. Of course after I had planted it Wendy said it would have looked much better in the back garden behind the garage, but it was too late then. And anyway, I wanted it in the front.

I've always wanted a rowan. When I was a lad my parents moved to a house called 'The Rowans'. They had two of the trees in their front garden. I've always loved their slender shapeliness, their lovely pinnate leaves and their clusters of creamy white flowers followed in the autumn by the red berries that the birds enjoy so much.

The night after I planted the tree, Becky and I went down the lane as usual. We take a wander down there every night and stop by the gate overlooking Joe's fields. We look at the moon and the stars. They are so clear and bright in the sky here. In fact, they give so much light that I often don't need my torch. Torch? Of course – we haven't any street lights up here.

I always stop when I want to look at the night sky. If I try to look at it while I'm walking, I become dizzy with my face turned upwards and I'm in danger of toppling over.

Leaning on the gate we look down over the town too. Its orange lights look warm and comfortable. 'Warm and comfortable' – it's funny the associations words often have. A German friend of mine once commented to me about something, '*Das ist varm and gumutlicht*'. I don't know any German and I don't know how to spell that phrase but whenever I think of something warm and comfortable I think of that friend.

On the other side of the town the main road climbs up into the hills. Cars coming down look almost like shooting stars with their lights zooming down to the town. Meanwhile, here in the lane, bats flit silently just above our heads and we hear the barn owls hooting and the foxes scream. If it wasn't all so lovely, and the moon and the stars so bright, it could be a bit eerie.

There was one really dark night when we were wandering back up towards our house and there was a great deep breath close beside our ears. Becky took off and never stopped until she was home. I was scared too, but it was only a bullock on the other side of the hedge. It's funny how you can get things out of proportion at night.

Anyway, as I was saying, the night after I had planted the rowan, we went down the lane as usual. Around the corner past the smallholding there was the most terrible racket you have ever heard. It was cats. Not just one or two of them – I should think every cat in the neighbourhood was there, all in a ring. And in the centre of the ring was Mr Feral Cat.

Yes, I've started to give him his full title. He's such a magnificent animal that he deserves proper respect. Anyway, all the cats except Mr Feral Cat were yowling their heads off. He was just washing his paws. The noise was so awful that Becky turned tail and made for home, so I did the same.

The next morning I met the man from the smallholding. 'How's things?' I asked.

'Not very good,' he said. 'Been selling my sheep. The bottom's fallen out of the market. There's no future in sheep so I've sold them all, all except those two up there. They're more like pets those two. My wife reared them on the bottle. How about you? How's things with you?'

'Fine. I've been planting some trees.'

'What have you planted?'

'A plum and three apple trees, just small ones.'

'Lovely, So you'll be having your own fruit. Nothing better,' he said.

'Oh, and I've planted a rowan by my front gate.'

'A rowan! Oh lord. That's done it.'

He turned and went striding off – perhaps 'striding' is not quite the word for a man of four-foot nothing. I had been going to tell him about the cats but I never got the chance.

The next thing we knew we saw him and his wife with their dog and their cats and their two favourite sheep, all in their car and towing their caravan. We never saw them again and their house went up for sale.

A couple of days later Joe called. He had been down moving his cattle from one field to another one, right in front of our garden. He climbed over the gate into the lane, came in by our front gate and round to the kitchen.

'Mornin' missus.' He always greeted Wendy the same way.

'Would you like a cup of tea or coffee?' she asked.

'Mug of tea would be nice, thank you.'

He drank his tea. I joined them in the kitchen and had a cup of coffee and we stood looking out at the garden while I told him about the cats.

'I've never heard anything like it in my life,' I said.

36

'Why do you suppose it was?'

'Who knows with cats?' he said. 'They're a law unto themselves. No one knows why they behave the way they do.' He paused and then said, 'I see you've been planting a few trees.'

'Yes. Come and have a look.'

So we went out into the garden.

'Pity you put that rowan in the front. When did you plant un?'

'The morning before those cats made that racket in the lane.'

'That's it then.'

I looked at him, puzzled. 'What do you mean?'

'You mean you don't know? My gor you don't know nothin' at all and that's a fact.'

My face must have been a complete blank because he laughed.

'You've planted a rowan without knowing the first thing about them. Witches *hate* rowans. They're magic. Because of that there tree, no witch will come anywhere near your house and that means they can't use the lane. That's why the cats were making such a noise. They were grieving for poor old Maud.'

'Who's old Maud?'

'*Old Maud*. Don't you know about old Maud? Gyaw. You buys a house in the country and you never check up on the locals before you come. You must be maised boy, proper maised.'

I hadn't heard that word since I was at school. He thought I was mad, but I still didn't know why. It must have something to do with this Maud woman.

'You still haven't told me about old Maud,' I said with just a hint of irritation in my voice.

'Old Maud is the local witch.'

'Oh for goodness sake,' I said. 'First it was fairies and now it's a witch. I wonder what it'll be next.'

'Don't you mock. I've told you about mocking before.'

'All right then. Where does this old Maud live?'

'Just down the lane,' he said.

'I've been down the lane dozens of times, hundreds even. I've never seen a house.'

'Ah,' he said, and he wouldn't tell me anything more about it.

He was *so* serious. But I knew Joe. I'd never known anyone who could pull your leg with such a straight face. All the same, I did decide that if there was anybody living down the lane that I didn't know about, it was high time that I found them and got to know them. So I determined that I would find old Maud if she really existed and lived nearby.

The Gypsy Caravan

The very next day Becky and I met a man down the lane. He was in the first part of the lane after it stops being a road and becomes just a bridle path. There he was busily working, tidying up one side of the lane and cutting back all the nettles and brambles.

The area he was working on seemed to be about the size of a large garden, roughly rectangular in shape. It was an odd place to be working because, as far as I could make out, the whole area was just one complete wilderness of nettles, brambles and trees sticking up out of the undergrowth. It was so thick you could imagine Sleeping Beauty in her castle hidden right in the middle of it. Tidying alongside the outer edge just along the lane seemed completely pointless. And what about the other side? I asked the man why he was doing it.

'Don't exactly know why,' he said, 'but I doos it every year. Every year about this time it sort of comes on me to up and tidy it. Don't get no rest until 'tis done. So I doos it, but I don't really know why.'

'It seems to be some sort of enclosed plot doesn't it? Why do you just work along the lane?'

'Well you wouldn't get through the lane if I didn't cut it back would you? And if you couldn't get through they'd bring one of they gurt big machines to cut it an' that wouldn't do at all would it? So I doos it.'

'Just along the lane.'

''As right, just along the lane.'

'Do you get paid for doing it?'

'No, I don't get paid. But then, in a manner of speaking, yes I do.'

I decided to wait while he sorted that one out in his mind.

'This yer garden,' he said (fancy calling it a garden, 'used to belong to a Gypsy a long time ago. I did little bits of jobs for her when she was alive. She used to travel all summer and then come back here for the winter. 'ad one of they old gypsy caravans pulled by a horse.'

'So who owns the land now?'

'There's someone somewhere,' he said, 'but I haven't never seed her.'

'But you still come and work here and you never get paid except...?'

'Oh ah. Well no I never get paid but I do sometimes find a few eggs or some fruit or vegetables lying by my back door. And that's the only way the old gypsy lady used to pay me so I reckon as how that's my wages still coming in.' He took off his cap and scratched his head. I found myself doing the same. I wished him good day and went on down the lane.

It cuts between two steep sides and with the trees overhanging it, it grows very dark; lovely and cool on hot summer's days. And then it opens out with scrub and woodland and a few magnificent ash trees on one side and wonderful open country and wide views on the other. And there are quite a lot of wild flowers too, so it's always a pleasure to walk along it. And if we see a roe deer or a fox or Mr Feral Cat, why that's a bonus isn't it?

We walked for about a mile and then turned left and left again, which brought us to a gate with a stile beside it. Becky squeezed under the gate and I climbed the stile. I stood and looked across at the sea, blue and calm in the distance. Should I walk through the fields or climb the hill and stroll across the top? It was such a lovely day I decided to make for the top and enjoy the views all round.

So we climbed. Becky amused herself chasing rabbits and I just enjoyed the scenery. It seems to change every few yards around here. We had crossed about half of the top of the hill when I found myself looking down on the other side of that rectangular wilderness. It really was thick, but as I looked I saw Mr Feral Cat stroll alongside the hedge and then slip inside the wilderness. It looked as though it was something he did regularly. I was curious.

I marked the spot from a couple of trees and then clambered down the hillside to have a look at his entrance. He had worn a path through the brambles but it was far too small for me. Becky might have managed it, but she wasn't interested.

I started to work my way alongside the wilderness, peering in at every tiny sign of a gap in the brambles and nettles. It wasn't easy and I didn't half get stung and scratched but I was determined to see in if I could.

There was a half barrel made of blue plastic lying in the field. The shepherd uses it to provide water when the sheep are on the hill. I put it up against the edge of the wilderness and climbed on top. Still nothing. I moved it along a bit. Nothing. But I was determined. I kept moving it a yard at a time and eventually I was rewarded.

There was a gap just large enough to see right in. It was amazing. Hidden in the midst of that wilderness there was an old gypsy caravan, but it was in beautiful condition. All the paintwork was fresh and bright with colour and the varnish and brasses were shining. In front of it there was a small garden with a tiny lawn and flowers and vegetables. And to one side chickens pecked at the ground in a large, wired off enclosure with a hen-coop at one end. This must be where old Maud lived. I'd found her home. How exciting.

At one end of the lawn there was a well. Near the door there was an open fireplace with a huge cooking pot over it. Mr Feral Cat was sitting on the lawn washing himself and basking in the sunlight. And leaning against the caravan by the door there was an old besom.

Besom? You don't know what a besom is? Surely you do. It's one of those old brooms made of sticks. You know, like a witch's broomstick.

I was fascinated. I stretched first this way and then that, trying with all my might to see a bit more, and then ... I fell off.

If I was scratched and stung before, that was nothing to the way I was scratched and stung now. 'Ow, ow, ow!' I yelled.

'He, he, he, serve him right. Nosy parker.'

That's what I heard but I didn't see anyone. It was time to go home. On the way we met the plumber's wife.

'What on earth have you been doing?' she said. 'You're scratched all over.'

'I fell in some brambles,' I said.

'Quite a fall if you ask me. Looks as if you rolled in them too.'

I passed it off as bravely as I could and then I asked her about the wilderness. I didn't tell her what I had seen.

'Yes,' she said, 'it's queer how Bill Humphries still comes every year and tidies up the lane. I believe there's still an old gypsy caravan in there somewhere.' And then as if she had said too much, she changed the subject. It was as if she didn't want to talk about it. That surprised me. She usually liked a good chat but when I tried to get her to talk about the caravan some more she just said, 'Standing talking won't get the work done will it? Must dash.'

And with that she was gone. So I went home too. Joe was there when I arrived, drinking a mug of tea. 'Gyaw look at he!' he exclaimed, roaring with laughter.

'I fell in some brambles,' I said with as much dignity as I could muster. But he and Wendy laughed so much that I took myself off to the bathroom to wash and cover myself with TCP. I decided not to tell anybody that I had found Maud's home.

42

Becky Stands Firm

A few nights after I had discovered old Maud's caravan Becky and I went down the lane as usual. It was the night of the full moon and the lane was bathed in light. I put my torch in my pocket and we strolled along without a care in the world. We stopped and gazed down over the town. We walked quietly on, rounded a bend in the lane and there were all the cats, not in a circle this time but in a semicircle right across the lane, blocking our path. Mr Feral Cat was just behind them and there, hovering just above them, sitting astride an old broomstick, was an old woman dressed all in black – black dress, black cape and black hat.

'Don't believe in witches don't you?' she cackled. 'Come all new into the lane with a dog have you? Trying to banish me from the lane with rowan trees are you? Well you needn't think you're going to get away with it. By the time we've finished with you tonight you'll want nothing better than to burn that rowan tree and that dog with it. She'll make a nice sacrifice on the altar of the rowan she will.'

I was horrified. And I was terrified. Terrified and horrified. Horrified and terrified. Which came first I wonder?

Becky wasn't. I've never thought of her as a brave, fierce dog. She jumps at the slightest thing. Look at her that night the bullock breathed at us. I've often wondered what she would do if either Wendy or I were threatened. But she's so soft and gentle and friendly that I never really thought she would be much use.

43

How wrong can you get?

She's not a pedigree collaborator for nothing. Her pedigree goes back generations, all nicely mixed: a bit of collie, a bit of labrador, a bit of German shepherd dog and who knows what else. Faced now with all those cats and that witch she stepped out from behind me and moved right in front of me. Her legs were stiff and tall, her back was arched and all the hair on her back stood straight up. She drew back her lips, revealing her fangs, snarling.

Mr Feral Cat was not over-impressed but all the other cats drew back. Even the witch was silent for a moment or two. Through her teeth Becky whispered to me, 'Play your flute.'

Did I tell you that I play the flute? Not very well I'm afraid. In fact if I'm honest, pretty badly really. Oh all right then, I'm hopeless. But I like playing it and living here is perfect. I carry it with me everywhere. When there's no one around I can play to my heart's content. No one hears me.

So when Becky said 'Play your flute' I did actually have it in my pocket. Though I was rather surprised that she should ask me to play. She doesn't like the noise any more than anyone else.

'What?' I replied.

Becky answered me a little more urgently, 'Play your flute.'

The witch urged the cats forward. But every one of them had been chased by Becky in the past and when they saw her standing there, snarling with her fangs bared, none of them was eager to be the first to attack. Mr Feral Cat cleaned his paws disdainfully.

The witch screamed at them, 'Attack, attack, attack!'

She darted forward to distract Becky and I took a swipe at her with my walking stick. She just grabbed it and snapped it in two as if it had been a twig. She cackled with laughter.

'Play your flute,' said Becky.

The cats had drawn closer. The witch swooped again, but she was also being a bit careful not to get too close to Becky's teeth. I tried to grab her broomstick but it just whacked me on the side of the head.

'*For goodness sake, play your flute!*'

Becky really seemed to mean it, so I did. There wasn't anything else I could do. The cats had drawn closer still. They were mewling and spitting and throwing out experimental claw-filled paws. Becky had lowered herself almost to the ground and watched and waited and growled dangerously. The witch was poised for a final attack. We hadn't a hope.

But when I played my flute they paused. Perhaps they had never heard such an awful noise in their lives. I don't know. Anyway, there was a moment or two's hesitation and then suddenly, the air all around us was full of bats.

Were they bats?

They darted about, all round the heads of the witch and the cats. Paws flew, hands flew, but they missed and missed and missed again, and still the bats were there, flying almost into their faces, forward and back, round and about. They never quite made contact but the air was full of them.

Only bats could fly like that surely. And yet there seemed to be the sound of hundreds of laughing, tinkling bells. That may have had something to do with the crack on the side of the head the witch's broomstick had given me. She was shrieking curses, waving her broomstick first this way, then that, but she never managed to hit any of the creatures either. She was as helpless as I had been only a few moments earlier.

The cats, all except Mr Feral Cat, flew in all directions through the hedges and were gone. Suddenly the witch was gone too. So were the bats. Everything had disappeared. Only Becky and Mr Feral Cat remained in front of me. The cat raised one paw, bent it across his chest and bowed. He really did. Becky also bowed with a slight lowering of her head and then she raised a paw and waved. I swear she waved. The two animals turned. Mr Feral Cat disappeared into the darker, wilder regions of the lane and Becky set off for home and bed.

I turned to follow and a bat flew around my head and laughed. A bat laughed? It really did. I suppose it was a bat. Whatever else could it be?

We turned in at the garden gate and took a final stroll round the garden. We passed the rowan tree and I touched it as if to say, 'No witch is going to make me get rid of you.'

And then we passed the compost heap. A pile of ragwort stalks lay on top of the heap. 'That's funny,' I thought. 'I haven't had any ragwort up. I wonder where they came from.'

We came round to the kitchen door. Wendy met us and asked, 'Did you have a nice walk?'

So I told her all about it. She didn't argue or tell me anything about witches not existing or anything. She just smiled her knowing sort of smile and said, 'Yes dear. Drink your Horlicks and get to bed.'

So I did. And I slept well. After all I had put old Maud properly in her place hadn't I? She wouldn't cause me any more trouble now...

Little did I know how wrong I was.

Warts etc.

The very next time Joe called, he was hardly sipping his tea when Wendy said, 'Did he tell you about the night he was attacked by a witch down the lane?'

For goodness sake. There are some things you just don't talk about. Especially to someone like Joe. He was the last person I would tell. I'd never hear the last of it. It wasn't fair. I don't go round spreading news of Wendy's intimate secrets do I? But then, I don't know whether she has any. She wouldn't tell me if she had.

But fancy telling Joe of all people.

'Ah, I'm not surprised,' answered Joe.

But Wendy was – surprised that is – surprised that Joe should seem to take it so seriously. 'Why's that?' she asked.

'Because of that there rowan he's planted by the front gate. Old Maud wouldn't be pleased. She don't like rowans one bit.'

'Old Maud?'

'The witch. Lives down the lane in the caravan.'

'No one can live in that caravan,' I said. Although if that was true, how was everything so spotless and fresh and the little garden so neat, and who looked after the chickens?

'You've seen it then?'

'Of course I've seen it.'

'Been all round it have you?'

'Yes if you must know.' His questions were making me feel quite ratty.

'So that's where you got yourself all scratched and stung

the other day I reckon,' and he laughed. 'Old Maud lives there all right.'

'But she can't do. There's no way in and no way out.'

'Maudy don't need no way in nor no way out.'

Wendy looked puzzled.

'She's got a broomstick,' I said.

'Oh,' she said, and nodded.

I didn't believe it. Here we were, three fully grown adults all talking perfectly seriously about a witch. But as I thought about all that had happened to me recently I felt that perhaps we *should* be talking perfectly seriously about her.

'Maud's all right really,' said Joe. 'I first got to know her when I was a boy. She seemed pretty old even then. I had some warts on my fingers and she blessed them. Wonderful the way she got rid of them for me.'

I remembered him telling me all that stuff when we were at school. All the country boys backed him up but I didn't believe it. It was all new to Wendy of course.

'How did she get rid of your warts?' she asked.

'With a spell. Let's think for a minute: "Warts have come and warts will grow, paint 'em with milk and warts will go".'

'And did she paint them with milk?' Wendy asked.

'Dandelion milk I expect,' I grunted.

'How did you know that?' asked Joe. 'My mother reckoned that was what it was.'

'It's an old treatment. Dandelions used to be used for all sorts of illnesses. And you can use their leaves in salads when they're young and fresh,' I said. I didn't tell them that I'd just read all this stuff in a book from the library.

'Hm,' said Joe. He had no intention of seeming impressed. 'How did you deal with Maud when she attacked you?'

Wendy did her best to keep a straight face. 'He played his flute!'

'Ah,' said Joe. 'That would do it. Brought in the fairies I

48

expect. That'll be why you had such a lot of ragwort stalks on your compost heap I suppose.'

'Ragwort stalks?' asked Wendy.

So Joe told her that fairies use ragwort to fly with, the way witches use broomsticks. Wendy did her best to look properly impressed but I could see she wasn't really swallowing it. She's got more sense.

Slugs and Snails

Did I tell you that Wendy bought me a greenhouse for Christmas?

I suppose it was to be expected really. All those years after she retired from work she was longing for me to retire too, so that we could be at home together. And then, as soon as I *was* at home she began to wish she could get me out from under her feet all the time. So she bought me a greenhouse. She was also hoping that it might take my mind off Old Maud.

I was pretty excited I can tell you. It came in one of those packs you assemble yourself. The instructions were in the pack and it was as straightforward as these things always are.

I wonder how many wrong ways there are of fitting a greenhouse together. I reckon I must have found them all. And that was in spite of all the trips I made to the garden centre to see the one they had on display and to study how they had put that one up.

I did get it up eventually. Only I had a few supports missing and about the same number left over. Well, exactly the same number left over as it happens. Wendy came out and showed me that the ones left over would fit the gaps if I put them in the way she suggested. So I tried her idea (when she wasn't looking) and it worked. Remarkable. I ended up with no gaps and no spares. How about that then?

Anyway, when the greenhouse was up, we went down to the garden centre and bought some seeds and some peat-free compost. Commercial extraction of peat is decimating the few remaining peat beds so it is crucial that we switch to peat-free products. I fished out all the old planting trays I had and sowed my seeds in the trays. I watered them and watched over them every day. To Wendy's surprise quite a lot of them came up. When they were big enough I transplanted them into pots and deeper trays.

Have you ever noticed how pots multiply in a garden? They are a bit like metal clothes hangers. Real fast breeders they are. I seem to be able to grow pots far more successfully than I can grow plants. But there I was in my greenhouse with lots of pots and trays and lots of growing plants. It really was exciting. I watered them and watched over them every day, waiting for the time when they would be big enough to plant out in the garden. Although when I looked at the garden I did worry a bit. Our predecessors had created such a complete garden that there didn't actually seem to be any room for more plants.

All this time of course, Becky and I were having our usual walks. We go out every morning and then in the afternoon Wendy takes us out again. Now that I had found where Old Maud lived I couldn't resist going and peeping over the brambles and nettles from time to time. One morning, Becky and I set out in the sunshine soon after there had been a long shower of rain. The air was beautifully fresh and clear but, I don't know whether you have noticed, when we have a shower like that all the slugs and snails come out. Our lawn was covered in them. We seem to grow all kinds, large and small, dark and pale, vegetarian and carnivorous, and slugs with a sort of flower on their tail like a sea anemone.

Anyway, we left them all behind and walked down the lane and then we came back over the hill. As we drew near to the wilderness I couldn't resist the urge to go down and have another peep. I climbed up onto the plastic half barrel and peered in. There was Old Maud herself. She was walking around her garden with a bucket, picking up all the slugs and snails. As she picked them up she sang in her tuneless way,

51

> Slugs and snails, slugs and snails,
> that's a spell that never fails.
> Slugs and snails, slugs and snails,
> pouring down like rain and hails.

And then she sang it again, on and on endlessly. I didn't really take much notice. It didn't seem to make any sense to me. But I did wonder what she did with the slugs and snails. Do witches eat them? I know French people eat snails, but I think they are a special kind.

The two ladies who live next door to us pick up the slugs and snails in their garden and throw them into the field below their hedge. I'm not sure how much use that is. I have visions of all those slugs and snails forming up like regiments of soldiers and marching straight back into the ladies' garden. Or perhaps they march into mine!

Is *that* why I've got so many of them?

It struck me that perhaps I'd better go round like old Maud and pick them up. Then I could take them out on my walks and drop them so far away that they would never bother to come back. So that's what I did. I waited for one of those showers that brings them all out and then I walked round the garden with my bucket singing my own kind of song. The leprechaun was not very pleased that I was using his bucket until I set him up in the shed with a little tot of the whiskey. Then he didn't mind. So I went round the garden singing,

> Blackbirds and thrushes,
> frogs and toads,
> come to the third house
> along our road.
>
> Come to my garden,
> eat all you can
> and make this old gardener
> a very happy man.

52

And while I sang, I picked them up. I don't mind picking up snails but slugs are a different matter. Their slime is so yucky and it's so hard to wash off afterwards. But I persisted and I collected a lot of them – hundreds. I called Becky and we walked out onto the other side of the hill, a good mile away, and then I emptied them all out. Let them go and eat grass for a change.

Feeling really pleased with myself, I spent the afternoon taking some of the plants out of the greenhouse and putting them in all over the garden. By half past four I was really tired. There were still hundreds of plants in the greenhouse but I had done enough for one day, more than enough. I was knackered.

I went to the kitchen door and asked Wendy for a glass of my favourite Dandelion and Burdock. Then I settled down in the sunshine with my drink. I sipped it slowly, sampling every mouthful, and then I put my sunglasses on, put the back down on my seat and leaned back for a well-earned rest. I think I must have dozed off because when I came to the sun had gone in and it was dark. Not night dark you understand, but cloudy dark, as if we were going to have rain. I shivered. And then I saw, flying in perfect 'V' formation like the red arrows, five ravens flying across the sky uttering that harsh croak of theirs. They were flying from inland (that's where the lane goes) towards us, which is towards the sea. And they were flying with their claws down. Each of them was carrying something.

Was it five ravens? The one in front looked different somehow, just as black but a different shape. As they drew nearer I saw what that lead flier was. It wasn't a raven. It was Old Maud on her broomstick. But what was she carrying? What were they *all* carrying?

Oh crikey. Oh no.

Pails!

I remembered her song:

Slugs and snails, slugs and snails,
that's a spell that never fails.
Slugs and snails, slugs and snails,
pouring down like rain and hails.

The first drops of rain began to fall, hard and heavy. I ran indoors and straight to the kitchen window. The rain was sheeting down. Old Maud and her ravens circled my garden three times and then each of them turned a pail upside down. I've heard of it raining cats and dogs but this was worse. A thousand times worse. There was nothing I could do.

Maud and the ravens flew away, the rain continued sheeting down and I went to my piano and poured out my misery and anger. I don't play the piano very well. In fact I'm pretty hopeless really. But just once in a while, when my emotions are stirred and my passions are in a turmoil I sit at that piano and play like a man possessed. It was stupendous, superlative. I got completely carried away until Wendy came in.

'What on earth is that awful noise?' she cried. 'I can't read my book when you're making such a racket!'

So I stopped, but my passion was spent anyway. I had a cup of coffee and settled down for a good read but I couldn't concentrate. I kept getting up and wandering over to the window, but night had fallen and I couldn't see a thing.

'What *is* the matter?' asked Wendy. 'You're like a caged tiger.'

I didn't think I'd better tell her I'd seen Maud flying over with her ravens, so I just said that I was worried about my new plants.

'Well it's no use worrying is it?' she said. 'You can't do anything about them until the morning. So calm down and I'll get you some supper.'

War

The following morning I walked round the garden. Almost all my beautiful new plants had been stripped. At first I felt nothing but despair but that was soon overtaken by a growing anger and determination. I was not going to be beaten. There were still a lot of young plants growing in my greenhouse. Somehow I was going to make sure that they were not demolished by slugs and snails. So I declared war.

After every shower of rain I went round the garden with my bucket and collected as many as I could. I took them out and dropped them the other side of the hill. And then I walked around the hill and collected slugs and took them home and put them in the garden.

'Are you mad?' asked Wendy. She already knew the answer to that question but she still asked it.

'These are a special kind of slug,' I said. 'Look at their tails. They all have a small shell on their tails like a thumbnail.'

'So they have,' she said, but they're still slugs.'

'Yes, but these are carnivorous slugs,' I said. 'They eat other slugs.'

'Hm,' said Wendy, 'and they probably eat runner beans as well.'

'To tell the truth, I wasn't sure about that, so I went to the garden centre to see what *they* had. Slug pellets can harm birds and pets so they were no use. There was some white stuff which was harmless to anything except slugs and snails. Perhaps I should try that. I read the instructions and then saw that it only protected plants for about four days. Four days! That was no use.

'Them's what you want,' said George from the garden centre. 'Them' were nematodes. 'They get inside all your pests and eat them up from the inside.'

'Hm. I don't think I like the sound of those,' I said. 'And what do they eat when they've finished with slugs? Isn't there anything else?'

'You could try gravel. Put that round your plants. Slugs won't go across gravel.'

I remembered being told in India that snakes wouldn't go across concrete and then I found three of them in our bathroom. The stairs to the bathroom were concrete. All our floors were concrete. 'The bathroom floor was bare concrete. If snakes crossed concrete I was pretty sure slugs would cross gravel. But it was worth a try. I bought some gravel.

And then a neighbour called in. 'I've got more runner bean plants than I need. Would you like some?'

'Ooh yes please,' said Wendy, ignoring the fact that I had grown some in the greenhouse which were just ready to go out. Wendy loves runner beans. She can't get enough of them. So our neighbour gave us a tray of runner bean plants.

'But how do you stop the slugs and snails from eating them?' I asked.

'Eggshells,' she said. 'Surround them all with egg shells. Slugs don't like egg shells.'

I have never eaten so many eggs in my life. We had boiled eggs, fried eggs, poached eggs, scrambled eggs, omelettes, egg custard, cakes made with eggs. It was unbelievable the things Wendy found to do with eggs, but then she does like runner beans an awful lot.

So I prepared the bed for the runner beans and put in all the bean sticks to carry them as they grew. I planted the runner bean plants and surrounded them with gravel and with egg shells and then I waited to see what would happen. But just to be on the safe side, I kept some of the plants back.

If it had been a football match instead of a war, I suppose you would have called it a draw. Some of those beans survived and some of them were eaten. But how did the slugs and snails get to them? I reckoned that they saw my defences, turned back and climbed up the hedge. Then they just jumped across and tucked in. Wendy thought that was daft.

'No,' she said, 'you just haven't put down enough egg-shells.'

I groaned. I knew exactly what that meant. Boiled eggs, fried eggs, poached eggs, scrambled eggs, omelettes, egg custard, cakes made with eggs ... But it was no use moaning. Wendy does like her runner beans.

And then Joe called in. 'Mornin' missus.'

'Morning Joe. Mug of tea?'

'Please.'

'Joe, do you grow runner beans?'

'Yes, course I do.'

'Then how do you keep the slugs and snails away?'

'Beer.'

'Oh I'm sorry. I've just made a mug of tea.'

'Yes, that's right.'

'But you just said you wanted a beer. Do you want that as well?'

As I joined them I found Joe laughing. 'No dear,' he said, 'the mug of tea is for me. The beer is for the slugs and snails.'

'Beer!' I exclaimed.

''Yes, they loves it.'

'So first they get drunk and then they climb my runner beans and eat them all the same.'

'No, stupid. You puts jars out near your runner beans. You plants the jars in the ground and then puts a couple of inches of beer in each jar. The slugs can't resist it. In they goes and drinks away and then drowns in it.'

'What a lovely way to go,' said Wendy.

'Are you serious?' I asked.

'Course I'm serious. I'm always serious,' he said.

But you never know with Joe. So that evening I put just a couple of jars out and in the morning I checked them. Joe was absolutely right. I got to work. I planted out the rest of my runner beans and all the other plants I still had in the greenhouse except the tomatoes – they were staying put. And everywhere I planted new plants, I planted jars of beer. There. Now we would see who had won the war.

That evening I took a stroll round the garden. It was amazing. There were regiments of slugs and snails – mostly slugs – heading towards their nearest jar. I could have danced for joy. Later on I went out with my torch. Have you ever heard slugs singing? Everywhere I went I heard the same refrain:

> Oh what a day,
> more beer I say,
> hic, hic, hooray,
> oh what a day.

I walked down the lane with Becky, feeling on top of the world, and as I walked I began to compose a song of my own:

> Slugs and snails, slugs and snails,
> drinking beer like drunken whales,
> jars and jars of slugs and snails,
> that's a bait that never fails.
> My beans and flowers will grow and grow,
> but that old witch will never know.

I was right too. We never had such a crop of beans as we had that year. Mind you, the caterpillars decimated my cauliflowers. I wonder if Old Maud had anything to do with that? I must ask Joe what to do about them next year.

The Day the Chimney-sweep Came

It was quite soon after the slug war that the chimney-sweep came. We've only the one chimney. It's for the anthracite boiler in the kitchen. I had been up and closed the chimney vent in the loft so everything was ready for him.

He needed a mug of tea to get him started. Joe arrived at about the same time – smelt the tea I shouldn't wonder.

'Mornin' missus,' he said, and then to the sweep, 'hello boy.'

'Mug of tea Joe.'

'I wouldn't say no.'

You bet he wouldn't. Wendy poured him one and then gave me a cup of coffee.

'You've planted a rowan tree by the front gate since I was here last,' said the chimney-sweep.

'Durned silly place to put un too,' said Joe 'It'll never do anything there. You should have put un down in the back with the fruit trees.'

'That's what I keep telling him,' said Wendy.

I didn't say a word. I wanted that tree where it was, and that was all there was to it. Call me obstinate if you like, but I wasn't going to budge just for them.

The chimney-sweep had been looking across the fields while we talked. 'You've got one or two ravens among those rooks,' he said. 'They've spread along the coast ever since they were released from Portland.'

I'd often thought we had ravens but never dared commit myself for fear of being laughed at for mistaking crows for ravens. But now, with one of those flashes of insight for which I ought to be famous, I knew exactly what he would be talking about next.

'I wonder if you've got any witches round here,' he said. 'Witches and ravens often work together, and witches and cats do. You've got a lot of cats around here haven't you?'

I knew it. They're all the same these country people. Can't stick to reality. Reality? Ah well, you know what I mean. I used to think I did too.

'Never mind witches,' I said. 'Just concentrate on the birds. There are quite a lot of different members of the crow family down there.'

The chimney-sweep was somewhat put out. 'You always find crows together don't you: ravens and rooks, crows and jackdaws, and magpies too.'

'Yes you do,' I said, 'but things seem to me to have changed since we were boys Joe.' I looked at him questioningly but he didn't respond so I went on, 'When we were boys I don't think there were so many crows about and they kept themselves to themselves more. And there certainly weren't as many magpies.'

'You may be right,' Joe answered. 'People don't shoot them as much as they used to. But memory is a funny thing and we haven't got any statistics have we?'

'No we haven't, and you're right about memory. But there are statistics for a lot of birds and they seem to tie in with our memories – well with mine anyway. Take thrushes and peewits and yellowhammers . . .' I couldn't think of any more offhand but they would do. 'There's nowhere near as many of any of those about as there were when we were lads. Statistics tell me that as well as my memory. So I may be right about there being more magpies and crows and about crows being more sociable.'

'How do you mean, sociable?' asked the chimney-sweep.

'When I was a boy I made up a rhyme: "a rook on its own is a crow, and a crow in a crowd is a rook". That was pretty true then, but it isn't so true now. You often find crows with rooks and jackdaws.'

'Crows don't nest with rooks though.'

'That's true,' said Joe, and pointed across the fields. 'Rooks have been nesting there as long as I can remember.'

If you let them, these country folk will go on chatting all day. Time never seems to matter to them. So I turned to the chimney-sweep and said, 'I expect you want to get on.'

'Yes,' he said, and went out to fetch rugs and cloths to cover the floor and all the airing cupboard shelves around the boiler and the nearest of the kitchen surfaces. Then he fetched his brushes and his vacuum unit. 'Do you mind going outside and checking when the brush comes out of the top of the chimney?' he asked.

So Joe and I went outside. 'That's for your benefit,' said Joe.

'Pardon?'

'He knows when his brush comes out at the top, but he wants you to see for yourself, so that *you* know.'

'Oh,' I said. Then I called into the kitchen, 'You've come right through. We'll leave you to it.'

Joe and I strolled down the lane and then he climbed over the gate and went to have a look at his cattle. They all came running and crowded round him as usual. He never left them long without a visit. I watched them surrounding him and pushing and shoving to try and get near. It was good to see such a close bond between them.

Becky and I went on down the lane and then climbed high onto the hill again. It was a lovely sunny morning and my irritability had vanished. I'd put the conversation about the rowan and witches and ravens behind me. I lay down in a hollow warmed by the sun, took out my flute and began to play. After a while I put it away and closed my eyes, basking in the sunshine.

Did I doze? Or did I really pop down to the wilderness to try to speak to Maud and make friends?

The way it seemed to me afterwards, we clambered down the hill. I'd have run down as a boy but I'm a bit more careful these days. Surely, if it had been a dream I would have run. Someone said that you're never old in your dreams. I don't know. Anyway we came to the edge of Maud's wilderness, stood the plastic half-barrel up again and I climbed up and peered through.

In the small clearing by her front door Old Maud had a fire going beneath that huge cooking pot – a cauldron I think they call it. And there she was with a kettle in her hand, circling round and round the pot and singing in a tuneless kind of voice, 'The west wind will blow, bring rain, hail or snow.'

I could have told her that. I'd heard the weather forecast too. These witches weren't so clever after all. But she was still circling round singing her rhyme:

> The west wind will blow,
> bring rain, hail or snow,
> and down that man's chimney
> each last drop must *go*.

With the word 'go' she poured some water from her kettle into the cauldron and then started all over again, singing her verse and pouring in more water. I nearly fell off the barrel again. It brought me to my senses with a start. I looked at my watch. Lunchtime. I must be getting home. So I stood up.

That's funny,' I thought, 'why did I have to stand up? And how did I get back to the top of the hill?' I looked down over the hill to the wilderness. Where was the plastic half-barrel? It was nowhere in sight. Anyway it was time to go home, so I went.

That night the weather changed. We had a howling gale

and the most dreadful rain storms. The rain came sheeting in from the sea and gave everything a real drenching. It was still at it when Becky and I went out in the morning. We got soaked right through. Never mind, Wendy would look after us when we got home.

I stripped off in the garden shed and ran into the kitchen. Did I say Wendy would look after us? I was hardly inside the house when she nabbed me.

'Have you seen *this*?' she cried and showed me a patch of damp around the flue where it comes through the kitchen ceiling. And there was water running down the outside of the flue as well.

'That crazy witch,' I thought. But Wendy brought me to my senses in no time at all. She's good at that.

'I suppose you forgot to open up the vent in the chimney after the sweep had gone. You *know* we get water down if you don't see to the vent.'

She was right of course. She always is. I'd got witches on the brain. So I hung my head in shame, confessed my sins and went up into the loft to open the vent. We had no more trouble after that.

Not with the chimney that is.

Mushrooms and Fish

It was early that September.

We were walking up on the hill and Joe was with us. The hill wasn't part of his farm. It belonged to a chap down the far side. But Joe loved it up there, anyone would. The views are superb and always changing. In his book *In the Country* (Hamish Hamilton 1972), Kenneth Allsop described being in our kind of countryside like this:

> It is not just a matter of being swallowed in the remoteness and haunted antiquity of the land. There is also a sense of being conjured with, of hallucination. It is halls of mirrors in series and in receding rows ... Take two steps in any direction and your surroundings are rearranged like the painted scenery of a toy theatre.
>
> It is a geological madhouse. A new hummock inflates before your eyes; an unsuspected valley has unfolded. It is easy to feel disorientated.

Wendy has sometimes got lost up here on misty days. But on this day it was clear all around, both looking out to sea and inland. The top of the hill is all ridges and hollows. There's hardly a level bit anywhere.

'See that village down there,' said Joe. 'All the older houses were built with stone from up here. That's why it's all so hummocky.'

I could have told him that. We passed the leaning black-thorn bushes, all grown sideways because of the wind up there. We walked on over the flattest part of the whole hill and then Wendy said, 'What on earth are those things?'

'Don't ee know?' said Joe.

'No. I've never seen anything like that in my life before.'

'They weren't here last week. Someone's dumped some great lumps of polystyrene I reckon,' I said.

'Why would they dump polystyrene up here?' asked Wendy.

Joe was looking at us with amusement. 'They're mushrooms,' he said.

'Mushrooms?' I exclaimed. 'For goodness sake, when will you say something sensible? Who ever saw mushrooms that size? And anyway, they don't even look like mushrooms.'

They didn't. They were huge. Bigger than footballs and pretty much the same shape. White they were, but no, they weren't polystyrene.

Joe picked one up. It had a very thin join holding it to the ground, like an umbilical cord He showed it to Wendy. ''Tis true it doesn't look like any other mushroom you'll ever see, but 'tis a mushroom all right. They call it a puffball. And if you've never seen one you ant never ate one neither. You've got a treat in store.'

'Eat it!' I said. 'I wouldn't touch it thank you very much. Not if it's a mushroom. Mushrooms are too risky. They're poisonous. My dad wouldn't even let us pick mushrooms. I don't want to be poisoned thank you.'

'Your dad was a nice chap, but he didn't know much about the country did he?'

'No.'

'Well 'tis like I said with the ragwort. When people tells ee to beware, what they really mean is that you got to take care. There is mushrooms that's poisonous, though most of 'em will only give you a bad turn. There's even some that can kill ee. Don't eat those pretty red ones in the Noddy books for instance. But if you know what you'm picking, you can have

65

some real treats with mushrooms, better'n anything you'll buy in the supermarkets.'

'And you can really eat that? asked Wendy, pointing to the puffball in Joe's arms.

'Oh yes. 'Tis delicious.'

'Hm,' I grunted, 'Seems a bit risky to me.'

'Oh you'm as bad as a friend of mine who won't eat fish.'

'Won't eat fish?' exclaimed Wendy. 'He must be mad.'

I don't like fish either except for tinned pilchards in tomato sauce (must be in tomato sauce) and prawns, but they're not really fish are they. Anyway, I stayed quiet.

'No he won't eat fish. When he was a little boy his sister swallowed a bone and had to be rushed off to hospital and he ant niver eat fish from that day to this.'

'I can understand that I suppose,' said Wendy.

'But the funny thing was, his son wouldn't eat fish neither. He always said he didn't like it, but he hadn't never tasted it.'

'Lots of children are like that with things they've never tasted,' I said.

'Don't interrupt when I'm telling you something. This boy married, and his wife liked fish. So she got pretty fed up never having it. One day she cooked two beautiful plaice and some vegetables and put it all on the table. She served the boy some vegetables and served herself some vegetables and one of the plaice. Then quite by accident, or so it seemed, she knocked off two or three mouthfuls of the other plaice but she left them on the serving dish. They started to eat their meal and the boy didn't dare to grumble. He got on with his vegetables. Then suddenly she said, "Oh, excuse me darling, there's something I want to see on television." She picked up her plate and ran into the lounge. When she came back to the kitchen with her empty plate her husband was already washing up. The other plaice had all disappeared. Had he put it down for the cat, she wondered?

She never said a word. About a month later they were

66

walking around the supermarket doing their weekly shop and he said, "Isn't it about time we had some fish? You haven't had any fish for ages and you know how you like it." She smiled to herself, and he's been eating fish ever since.'

'But fish,' I said in a superior tone of voice, 'is not like mushrooms. Fish is not poisonous.'

'Nor is this puffball,' said Joe. 'Not as long as you eat it while 'tis still pure white.'

'But how do you cook it?' asked Wendy.

We were nearly home by now.

'I'll come in and show ee if you like,' said Joe. 'Then if you like un you can keep half and I'll take half home to my Barbara.'

So in he came and I have to admit that even I was interested by now. He took the bread knife and cut off a few slices.

'There,' he said. 'Just coat they in beaten egg and bread crumbs missus and fry 'em in butter.'

Wendy got busy and when she had finished we all sat down at the kitchen table. I hate to admit it but the puffball was delicious. We kept our half and I kept pestering Wendy to cook some more until it had all gone.

We didn't pick any more from the top of the hill. There were too few for that and we thought we'd better leave some in the hope that there might be some the following year. But we searched and searched on all of our walks to try to find some more. We hunted everywhere, but we didn't find any. It was so disappointing.

We did begin to find some parasol mushrooms about. They were all right but not a patch on the puffball. And the garden was demanding attention the way it always does as summer turns into autumn. I set to, to tidy up my hedges and the beds in front of them. It is incredible how much growth there is to cut back. I worked my way round one of our great hydrangea bushes to the hedge behind and there, staring me in the face, was a puffball, grown in our own garden. It was irresistible.

Joe had set me off of course. After he introduced us to that first puffball I got out the best book I had with mushrooms in it and settled down to study it. That's how I got to know about parasols. There were ninety-three different kinds of fungus in that book and twenty-nine of them were listed as edible. I didn't really fancy some of them, and I wasn't sure I would get the recognition of some of the others right so they were to be left alone. Yet, of all those ninety-three, only eight were down as poisonous. Joe was right. The message should not be 'beware', but 'take care'.

Later that month and in October, as the last swallows were flying around overhead and gathering on the telephone wires, and as the goldfinches were feasting on the thistle-down, I began to find field mushrooms. Sometimes they were so big that I wondered if they were horse mushrooms. I was never quite sure but they were both safe so it didn't matter. And they were delicious too.

Grandmother's Lace Shawl

Someone at an interview once asked me what my faults are. How stupid. Surely she could see that I haven't any? Ask Wendy.

Actually, no, I think I'd rather you didn't.

But if I *do* have a fault it is that I do go on a bit when I've something on my mind. Which is why, as Christmas drew near, Wendy bought me a book.

'There,' she thought, 'that'll take his mind off witches for a while.'

She was right. It did. Poor Wendy, she was to wish that she had never found that book. I'd better tell you about it.

You know how it is at Christmas. The children are all excited and wake up early to see if Father Christmas has come – so I was up at five o'clock as usual. When I saw from my stocking that he had come I woke Wendy up too. After all, half the fun of being excited over your presents is sharing the excitement with someone else. Actually, when I woke her I gave her a cup of tea. She doesn't seem to mind being woken up quite so much if she has a cup of tea.

There were presents in her stocking too, so she could be excited it she wanted to, though of course I knew what they all were, so they didn't seem very exciting to me.

We had decided to go across to Charmouth that morning to watch the swimmers. As we were up so early we went across early to give Becky a walk on the cliffs. We arrived at the car park by the beach at about eight and for a long time we just sat in the car watching in amazement.

Seagulls were flying inland. Not just one or two – there were thousands and thousands of them flying inland. We had never seen anything like it. We hadn't seen birds in such vast numbers, not since we lived in Surrey. Watching the seagulls reminded me of the great waves of bombers we had seen going over in the war. A continuous river of seagulls flew overhead. It was ages before the river dwindled to a few stragglers and then stopped altogether.

When they had gone we climbed up the cliffs to Stonebarrow, walked for a time on the top, admiring the glorious sea views, and then slithered and stumbled our way down again in time to see the swimmers. They come every year and brave the elements to raise money for the Royal National Lifeboat Institution.

When you live close to the sea you become much more aware of all that the lifeboat crews risk and achieve. It's amazing that they do it all without public funding. We watched the swimmers and put our Christmas gifts into the collecting box, and then it was time to go home and get on with our own Christmas celebrations.

'Are you sure you've emptied your Christmas stocking properly?' asked Wendy.

'Yes,' I said, and told her all the things I'd had.

'I think I'd go and make doubly sure you've really emptied your stocking right down to the toes,' she said.

So I went and fetched my stocking. Wendy was right of course. She always is. There was a small book that I hadn't noticed. I took it out and carried it into the lounge. Wendy placed a cup of coffee by my side but I hardly noticed. The book was about a girl called Mary Anning who lived in Lyme Regis.

Born in 1799 she learned from her father about the fossils on the beach. She and her brother Joseph were always down there. In 1811 one of them found an ichthyosaur. That was probably Joseph, but soon afterwards Mary found a plesiosaur. These things created tremendous excitement because nobody knew anything about such creatures.

It wasn't long before we were in Charmouth again. After Christmas the weather turned very cold and we heard that the river at Charmouth had frozen over. So we went across to see. It really was frozen hard. The poor old ducks were having a right struggle, slithering about all over the ice. We watched for a while and then went down onto the beach and set off east towards Golden Cap. The cliffs all along this coast are collapsing into the sea bit by bit, which is why people find so many fossils. Mostly the falls are small and hardly noticeable, or there's just a stream of horrible grey slurry pouring down. But sometimes huge collapses take place.

So we kept well away from the cliffs as we walked along the beach. We watched the sea, but I was also busy scanning the cliffs and the beach. It would be so exciting to find a fossil.

The sun was low and I had my sunglasses on. Suddenly Wendy pointed out to sea.

'What are those?'

'What?'

'Those out there.' She raised her binoculars to her eyes but I could see them quite clearly now through my sunglasses.

'They're ichthyosaurs,' I said excitedly. 'Good heavens, real live ichthyosaurs.'

Ichthyosaurs? You dolt,' she said. 'Don't be so daft. They're dolphins.'

I didn't argue. It's never any use arguing with Wendy. She always thinks she's right. But I know what I saw, so there.

We walked on along the beach and I was beginning to get tired. 'When are we going to turn back?' I asked. 'I'm not walking all the way to the foot of Golden Cap.'

'We'll just walk as far as the waterfall,' said Wendy.

71

I didn't want to walk all that way. It's almost as far as Golden Cap. The waterfall falls onto the beach just below St Gabriel's. I looked at it. We weren't all that far away. Oh, if that's what she wants, I thought. So I plodded on.

The beach was all pebbles so it was pretty hard going. You can never be quite sure with these beaches. Sometimes they're all pebbles, sometimes they're all sand. Sometimes they're quite easy to walk on, sometimes every footstep is hard work. It was hard work that day, harder and harder the nearer we got to the waterfall. And then suddenly all the hard work was forgotten.

'Just look at that,' said Wendy. 'It's beautiful.'

So it was. The sunlight played on it and gave it colour and dancing light. It was radiant and alive and glittering, a structure of such beauty that its difficult to describe or comprehend. It reminded me of something but it was a while before I could pin it down. We walked all round it, admiring it from all sides. It really was fantastic. Yes, I knew. It was like my grandmother's lace shawl only white. It was like the lace trimmings my aunt used to make for altar cloths and dining-room tablecloths, or rather, it was like hundreds of them placed one on top of the other, all overlapping as they hung in serrated layers. The waterfall had frozen solid and become one of the loveliest sights we had ever seen in our lives.

We had to drag ourselves away but we hardly noticed the long trek back to Charmouth and the car. To be truthful I don't think we would have done anyway because as we walked back along the beach the sun began to set.

There is something special about a sunset over the sea. You could imagine great caverns of molten lava on the horizon as if you were peering right down into the depths of the earth where the fires bubble and burn beneath the volcanoes. The sea and the sky were both alight with colour: deeper colours on the sea, rippling and shining all the way from the horizon

72

to the shore. And in the sky a multitude of different pinks tinted the clouds and made them blush when we told them how beautiful they were. This really is another world you know.

'It s magical,' sighed Wendy.

Barnacles, Reptiles and Birds

We went back several times to see grandmother's lace shawl. Every time we were thrilled by it. The breadth of it across the cliff top and the length of it hanging down seemed to take us by surprise every time we saw it. But inevitably the thaw came and it returned to its normal state.

By that time we had something closer at hand to enjoy. The snowdrops were out, thousands of them right down the side of our garden. They were spectacular. So was the weather. It broke again and we had some tremendous storms. One night we sat in the conservatory and watched an incredible display of lightning running across the hills twenty miles away. It went on for three quarters of an hour.

But with all the storms the lanes around us became real quagmires. So we took to going down to the beaches for our walks and watching the seas crashing in. It was on one of those walks that I became aware of Wendy standing with something at her feet. She was twenty or thirty yards ahead of me. She usually is. I can't keep up with her.

What was it? It looked like a ball but it must have been more interesting than that to persuade her to stop and wait for me. It was a ball of cork from a boat or a fishing net. It was a good deal bigger than a tennis ball and covered in goose barnacles. I'd never seen such a thing before.

With the arrival of February the weather calmed down again and we had a couple of weeks of glorious, cold, still, sunny days. One afternoon we decided to cross the down and walk to the beacon up on the cliffs. It's one of our favourite walks. In some ways winter is the best time to cross the down. In summer the bracken closes up all except the main paths and I spend a good deal of time keeping those open. But in winter the main paths are free and so are all the side paths; the tracks used by deer and foxes and badgers.

We climbed the first part of the down and stopped to catch our breath and look at the view. And then we turned right onto a side path. There's a bit of a clamber across a gully and then another climb. As we began to climb again Becky darted off and we stopped to watch. Sure enough, two roe deer rose from the gully and ran across the down, away from us. We often see them there.

We passed a field with sheep in it. In the midst of the flock we saw a fox sitting enjoying the winter sunshine and having a good scratch. A couple of fields and a couple of stiles later and we were out on the cliffs by the beacon, looking down at the sea.

Wendy looked at the views east and west through the binoculars. I had my sunglasses on as usual. I seem to wear them more in the winter when the sun is low than I do in the summer when it is high overhead. Flying low over the water I saw two birds. They had to be birds didn't they? What else would be flying low over the water?

Were they birds? I pushed my sunglasses tighter up against my nose. It's so irritating the way glasses slide down, especially when you're looking at something down below. I've even had them fall off before now.

I looked again, more carefully this time. Good heavens! This was confirmation of what I saw the other week if anything was. Of course it was no use saying anything to Wendy.

'What are those birds?' she asked.

Ah, so she had seen them too. I wondered what she would make of them. Would she realise that they were not birds at all? No, they were pterodactyls, that's what they were. The kind called dimorphodons, the same sort that Mary Anning had found.

'Have a look at them through the binoculars,' Wendy said. 'They look like cormorants to me.'

Cormorants! Poor old girl, her eyesight's not what it was.

I took the binoculars. Hm. They did look a bit like cormorants. Quite a bit like cormorants really. I handed the binoculars back.

'Could be,' I said, and put my sunglasses back on. Those weren't cormorants. No way. They were dimorphodons. But I decided to keep my mouth shut.

Wendy went on studying the sea and the coastline. It was a clear day so we could see right round from Start Point to Portland. As she looked this way and that and swept the sea with the binoculars I went and sat down. Whoever put that seat up by the beacon did oldies like me a real service.

Cormorants? Dimorphodons? I mused. What did it matter really? Oh I know that there are people who will travel hundreds of miles to try to see something they have never seen before. But it has always seemed to me that Lao Tse had it about right all those centuries ago.

Lao Tse was a Chinese philosopher who lived in about the sixth century BC. He wanted to achieve harmony with the spirit of nature and the universe. Taoism derives from him. No I'm not a taoist, though I can't imagine a better goal than the one he set himself. Lao Tse said that he could see the whole world from his window, or something like that. And I was wondering whether it really mattered whether I was seeing a dimorphodon or a cormorant. I thought of the pleasure cormorants have given me over the years.

I've watched them ever since I was a boy. Goodness knows how many times I've watched them dive and tried to guess where they would emerge. I've always been wrong. And hundreds of times I used to hold my breath until they surfaced. At least, I tried to but I nearly always failed with that too.

'Are you going to sit there all day?' The question was kindly put. 'If you want to have a doze you'd do better in the armchair at home,' Wendy added.

So I hauled myself to my feet and we turned inland towards our home. As we set off there was a cry overhead. We both looked up. I didn't have my sunglasses on any more but there was no mistaking it. Circling easily, lazily, resting on the air currents, was a buzzard. Gliding gently round and round, it circled the whole area. Then it leaned slightly sideways and with scarcely a flap of its wings it swept inland the way we were going. Effortlessly it crossed the sky until it was out of sight.

My excitement at seeing the dimorphodon was more than matched by this magnificent bird of the present. I wonder how many generations of them have flown across these hills and cliffs? I felt utterly content.

We walked back across the fields and over two stiles, and then downhill from the down to the main road. We crossed the road into our lane and were home in no time.

On Cogden Beach

We don't very often go to Cogden Beach. It's such a long way away. And so expensive – all that petrol. It must be all of six miles – *each way*. So I only take Wendy there for a special treat.

Where is Cogden Beach? It's part way along the vast Chesil beach; shingle all the way along from West Bay to Portland with a bit of sand at the West Bay end.

We walked down from the car park and then took the inland path towards West Bexington. That gives Becky a good run before we make her endure the shingle. There was a dirty old tramp walking behind us – no, not an *old* tramp, a young one. It could have been disconcerting but he kept his distance, about thirty yards behind us. We weren't unduly worried but we did keep half an eye on him.

We turned off the path and crossed the bridge down to the beach. Crunch, crunch, crunch. That shingle really is hard work to walk on but we weren't in any hurry. That helps. Crunch, crunch, crunch. Oh blow it, that tramp had come down onto the beach as well.

The beach descends in a series of ridges to the sea. We threw a stick or two for Becky and walked down to the ridge above the sea and there we sat down. The tramp did the same, about fifty yards from us, so we didn't feel threatened in any way. And there was absolutely no one else in sight.

It was a perfect day, warm in the sunshine but not too hot. Just the lightest of breezes played on our faces and on the face of the water. It was almost flat calm, but not quite. There was a gentle swell and the water played quietly with the shingle as it surged a little towards us and then sucked itself back again. It was a glorious shade of blue overall, but close in where the tiny wavelets broke it was almost transparent in its purity. And as we looked along the vast length of the beach the blue was fringed with just a slender strip of white.

I put on my sunglasses, those magical sunglasses, and we sat and basked in the warmth of the sun. We lay back and dozed and then Wendy interrupted the peace of the afternoon.

'Oh look,' she said, 'three black Australian swans, or are they cormorants?'

They were flying towards us from Abbotsbury where the swannery is so it was natural to think of them as swans, but I doubted it. Cormorants were more likely. They were coming closer now. It would be easy to tell in a minute. What did it matter anyway? It was so lovely and warm. I lay back again, contented and dozy.

'They're dimorphodon,' I murmured.

'What on earth are dimorphodon?' asked Wendy.

'They're a kind of flying reptile,' I answered. 'A bit bigger than a goose but smaller than a swan.'

'I can see what size they are,' she said irritably, 'but I've never heard of dimorphodon . You're having me on.'

'No I'm not. They're a kind of pterodactyl. Mary Anning found the skeleton of one near Lyme Regis in 1828.'

'Mary Anning? She was that fossil hunter wasn't she, the one who became so famous?'

'Yes, that's right.'

'So how can we be seeing dimorphodon when they died out all those millions of years ago?'

'I don't know. We do see things round here don't we? They were dimorphodon all right – unless they were a coven of witches in disguise.'

'Witches!' she sniffed. 'You've got witches on the brain.'

There was a long pause, a moment of blissful quiet and then she was at it again. 'Ooh look, look!' She had the binoculars to her eyes. 'Just look at that young tramp.'

Unwillingly I heaved myself up onto my elbows. The birds, dimorphodon, witches, whatever they were, had no sooner passed over the tramp than he stood up, whirled around three times and stripped off all his clothes before rushing into the sea.

'Oh,' said Wendy, 'wouldn't it be wonderful to do that.'

'We haven't brought our costumes,' I said.

'No, silly, not with costumes. Just like that man.'

'There are too many people around,' I said grumpily. I didn't want to make a fool of myself even if she did. I lay back on the beach and then I became aware that there really were too many people around. A great throng of women came plodding along the beach from West Bexington with a huge banner carried in front of them. It was just like one of those banners you see at Trade Union marches. As they came closer I saw that it said proudly, 'West Bexington Mothers' Union'. Those women looked pretty stern and determined.

'Poor chap,' I thought, 'he's for it now.'

And then I heard the band. I turned and there they were, marching across the shingle from Burton Bradstock. It was the band of the Royal Marines. I knew them because they had been on television. There'd been a series about them on *Spotlight South West*. But I'd have known them anyway. After all I was in the Navy, remember? And there behind the band came the ship's company of my ship: HMS *Defiance*.

Where did I go in the Navy? What did I do in the Navy? Look, I do wish you wouldn't interrupt, I lose my train of thought. Ah yes, I know. It was incredible how smart they managed to look marching on the shingle. The band was brilliant with the sun shining on the instruments. And the ship's company marched behind them with just that hint of informality, just the merest soupçon of casualness which

80

marks out the seaman from the soldier and demonstrates the fact that the Navy is the senior service. Perfect.

And then those dimorphodon flew overhead once more.

I have never seen anything like it. The ship's company did a perfect 'off caps', cheered, and started to strip. Good heavens! Some of them were women!

The bandsmen put down their instruments, took off their pith helmets and began to strip too. And some of *them* were women. **It wasn't like that in my day.** Oh no.

I turned away. This was no fit sight for masculine eyes. Help! On the other side of us the Mothers' Union had cast aside the banner and all the members were discarding their clothes as fast as they could go.

'Wonderful!' cried Wendy, 'oh wonderful!' And she leapt to her feet and followed suit, rushing into the sea with the whole mêlée from both sides of us.

Have you ever sat fully clothed on a beach on a hot day while all the world is going mad around you? It is a most humiliating experience I can tell you. It is no pleasant thing to be the odd one out, even if you are the only one who is not odd, if you see what I mean.

Discreetly and quietly I took off my clothes, folded them neatly and slipped into the water. It was warm. Yes it really was. Warm and soothing like a bath. I'm not a very good swimmer but I lay on my back and gently cruised around with minimal use of my hands and legs. It was so beautifully restful. The fact that Becky was racing up and down the beach barking her head off barely touched my consciousness at all. Once or twice she swam out and butted me but I couldn't be bothered with her. This was bliss.

When I finally turned over and took stock of my surroundings I discovered that there were only two of us left in the water the tramp and me. And on the edge of the water, fully clothed, stood the members of the Mothers' Union looking very fierce indeed and crying, 'Out! Out! Out!'

81

Where was Wendy? Oh help, I needed Wendy.

She was also fully dressed. She was sitting by my clothes and looking very amused.

I stayed floundering around, wondering what to do, but the tramp swam steadily towards the women and then rose from the water and strode towards them. He looked rather like that giant at Cerne Abbas. In fact, in one respect he looked exactly like that giant at Cerne Abbas. The women shrieked and fled higher up the beach to where the band was playing. Thanks to the ridges of shingle, the band was now completely out of sight.

As the women fled I took my opportunity and heaved myself out of the water like a rather pathetic and misshapen seal. I struggled across the stones to Wendy. You'd have thought she would have thrown my shoes to me.

'You might have seen dimorphodon,' she said, 'but I've just seen an ichthyosaur.'

'Where?' I cried excitedly. 'That's another of the creatures Mary Anning found: icthyosaurs and plesiosaurs.'

'Plesiosaurs looked a bit like the Loch Ness monster didn't they?' asked Wendy.

'Yes and ichthyosaurs more like a dolphin or a whale.'

'Then it's an ichthyosaur I can see,' she said.

'Where? For goodness' sake tell me where. Here, give me those binoculars.' I was so excited that I forgot to say 'please': I just grabbed them.

'I don't need binoculars. I'm looking at it now,' she said.

It was so frustrating. I tried to take a line from the direction in which she was looking but it didn't seem to make sense. How could she see anything at all? She was looking at *me*.

Oh!

Very funny. But I was not amused. With all the dignity I could muster I put on my clothes and we strolled up to listen to the band. The ship's company was dancing with tremendous gusto, still wearing full birthday suit rig. The ladies of the Mothers' Union mingled with the seamen and seawomen (surely they don't call them seapersons nowadays?) and danced with equal vigour and perhaps a touch more grace. The tramp had been sucked into it all.

He was enjoying himself so much that when a chief petty officer placed a recruiting form in front of him he signed it with scarcely a cursory glance. Nor did he seem unduly ruffled or surprised later when he was issued with a uniform and carried off in the midst of the ship's company. But I digress.

Wendy and I also found ourselves swept into this mass of dancing dervishes. We danced and danced until at last the bandmaster called a halt. He turned to face us.

'That was magnificent,' he said.

He was pretty magnificent too.

'You all deserve prizes. Queue up on my left please.'

There was the most unholy scramble for places in the queue. It was rather like the opening of a jumble sale. As you can imagine, the women brushed us men aside like flotsam and fought one another for places at the front. Wendy was up there with the best of them. Then came the men of the ship's company with the tramp safely in their midst. I brought up the rear. Each and every person received a prize – a pebble from the beach.

The ladies of the Mothers' Union formed up behind their banner and strode off back to West Bexington, sweeping up the tramp's old clothes as they went. They could be burned. They were determined to keep their beach clean.

Wendy gave me her pebble for safe keeping and we went back to where we had been sitting. I placed the pebbles with our things and lay back in the sunshine. I felt just like a boy who has been awarded first prize in a school prizegiving.

Wendy nudged me. 'Come on,' she said, 'the tramp has gone. There's no one about. If we don't go in soon we shan't get a swim at all.'

Shan't get a swim? What on earth was she talking about? But she was obviously utterly serious. She was stripping off at a rate of knots. Oh well. I clambered to my feet and did the same.

The sea was nowhere near as warm as I expected it to be, but it was very pleasant all the same. I lay on my back and paddled around gently using my arms and legs no more than I had to. Becky barked at the water's edge and then swam out to check that we were all right. She butted me in the ribs and swam back to the shore.

I finished my swim long before Wendy. She's a much stronger swimmer than I am, and women seem to be able to stay in longer than men anyway, don't you find?

She finished her swim, we dried ourselves in the warmth of the sun, dressed and went home. But if you think much of this was just a dream, you're quite wrong. Out in our garden where I placed them proudly that day, I can show you the very pebbles the bandmaster gave us as prizes.

The New Car

As we drove home from Cogden Beach, Wendy was silent. She often is. We can drive for hundreds of miles and hardly say a word. It doesn't matter. Our silences are very easy and companionable.

We arrived home and had our tea while we watched the news. I can't abide the national news. It's so depressing and mostly about foreign parts like London. So I watch the headlines and then switch over to Carlton's local news. When that has finished I watch BBC's *Spotlight South West* with Wendy and then we settle down for the evening.

She was still very quiet. If we had been in the car I might have asked, 'Penny?' And she'd have said 'No thank you.' And I'd have said, 'No, I didn't mean "do you want to spend a penny". I meant, "a penny for your thoughts".' And she'd have replied, 'I'm not thinking.' And that would have been that.

As we were at home I just asked, 'What are you thinking about?'

'Nothing,' she answered.

But I knew she was thinking about something. I was right too. She was thinking about dinosaurs.

She had given me that book about Mary Anning to take my mind off Old Maud. Now she needed to find something to take my mind off dinosaurs. At last she said, 'Our car's getting terribly rusty.'

There it was, right out of the blue. A sentence snatched from nowhere. She's just like a magician producing rabbits from a hat.

'Yes it is,' I said, 'but you love that old car.' It was true. It was an old turquoise Toyota Carina, an automatic that had cost us £800. We had driven it and driven it mile after trouble free mile. Goodness knows how old it was now but it was well into its second hundred thousand miles.

And it was getting pretty rusty.

'Perhaps it's time we thought about a replacement,' she said sadly.

'If we do, we could do with a small camper van.'

'It would have to be a *very* small camper van,' she said.

You know how it is with these things. They're like having your appendix out or having your hip done. As soon as the subject is broached you meet everybody else who has had the same things dealt with. We had no sooner broached the subject of a camper van than I found a firm just beginning a promotion for a baby Daihatsu Hijetta. They would actually come and show us one. And they did.

I knew we were sunk as soon as I saw the salesman: young, blond and bronzed and in spite of all that, a very pleasant man to talk to. He didn't push for a sale. He simply showed us round the vehicle and let it sell itself. It was incredibly small but there was an amazing amount in it. We were hooked.

So it was farewell Carina and hello Hijetta. Wendy named it 'Pip Squeak' straight away and inwardly she was smiling all the way from the bank. She knew what men are like with cars – even such a tiny little vehicle as this. There'd be no more talk of dinosaurs. At a stroke, she thought she had taken dinosaurs and Old Maud off the conversation menu for good.

But as it happened, things didn't work out quite like that. And to make matters worse, Joe went hysterical when he saw our fine little camper. He would wouldn't he? He drives one of those Land Rover things when he's not driving a tractor.

In spite of Joe, for a while I was like a child with a new toy. Come to that, Pip Squeak was rather like a toy. But then November arrived.

I don't like the noise of fireworks. I never did, not even as a boy. But we can sit here in our conservatory high above the town and look down and watch the fireworks fly high up into the night sky and then burst in all their glory, and we don't hear a sound.

It was the day after bonfire night that I had to go to Axminster. I don't remember the reason why but Wendy chose not to come. That was unusual for a start. She comes everywhere with me so that we can enjoy those conversation-free chats of ours. Luckily as it turned out, I left Becky at home too.

I set off in little Pip Squeak along the A35 past Charmouth. I climbed over the top of the hills north of Lyme Regis and into Devon. Before long we had another climb up Raymond's Hill. Pip Squeak is a bit slow when it comes to climbing so I was very conscious of everything behind me and wondering how I could best let it pass.

There seemed to be a fair bit of mist behind me on the climb, which was strange because it was a lovely fine day. No, it wasn't mist. But surely my exhaust shouldn't be smoking, belching out stuff like that ? It was a new car, for goodness sake. I thought perhaps I ought to take a look so I pulled into the first layby I came to. As I did so a car raced past with a lady leaning out of the passenger window pointing at my car. How rude! Some people! Make a fuss about the least little thing. I got out and strolled round to have a look.

Oh wow!

Pip Squeak was on fire. 'That damned witch,' I thought. Why had I suddenly thought of Old Maud. I hadn't thought of her for months. 'At least she won't know that I've got a fire extinguisher.'

I pulled it out and before long I had the fire not just under control but out. Then I had a look around and discovered that I was in luck. There was a telephone box not far up the road. I phoned the RAC and in due course they sent me a giant pickup truck to take us to the Daihatsu garage.

Jim the foreman had a good look at the poor little thing. He sucked in through his teeth. 'Can't understand that,' he said. 'It's new isn't it?'

'Brand new,' I said.

'Never known such a thing to happen before,' he said. 'You haven't been playing with fireworks have you?'

'No,' I answered. I wondered whether to tell him about Old Maud and decided that perhaps it might be better if I didn't.

'We'd better have a proper look at it,' he said. 'so you'll need something to get you home.'

'Yes I will,' I answered.

'We can arrange that for you,' he said, and they lent me a car which I could keep until they had sorted out poor little Pip Squeak.

It was a couple of days later that he rang me up. 'We've had a good look at your vehicle and we've no idea why she caught fire. I've never known such a thing to happen before. We'll repair it of course, free of charge.'

'I don't think I'm going to feel safe driving her again if you haven't been able to find anything wrong.'

'No,' he said. 'Perhaps I'd better have another look.'

It was another couple of days before he rang me again.

'We've repaired your car,' he said.

'And have you found out what caused it to catch fire?'

'No,' he said.

'She's a brand new vehicle,' I said.

'Yes,' he said. 'Perhaps I'd better have a word.'

'I'd be grateful if you would.'

Half an hour later he rang again. 'I've had a word,' he said.

'And?'

'And we'll give you a new vehicle to replace the one that caught fire.'

'Excellent,' I said.

'Only there's a snag.'

Isn't there always.

'Go on.'

'There aren't a lot of these kind of vehicles about.'

'That's true.'

'And we'd rather like our vehicle back.'

'So?'

'We'd like you to take your vehicle. Then you can either wait until the makers supply us with another one, which could be some time, or you could drive across to their factory and then they'll give you one straight away.'

'Fine. Where's their factory?'

'Sussex.'

'*Sussex*!' I exclaimed.

He was careful to make no comment and after a pause I said, 'OK. I'll go to Sussex and fetch my new car myself.'

So we made arrangements for me to pick Pip Squeak up and when I did we made arrangements for the trip to Sussex. I wasn't too happy having to drive there in a car which had caught fire for no discernible reason, but what else could I do?

I was beginning to lose patience with Old Maud.

A Trip to Sussex

Quite a lot of our family live in Sussex and Surrey. Given my surname that's not surprising. It's a Sussex name. So I thought that Wendy would love to come with me to collect Pip Squeak Mark 2. Then we could spend a few days doing the rounds and showing off our new camper van.

'Not on your life,' she said. 'You needn't think I'm going all that way in a car that bursts into flame.'

I did my best to persuade her but I have to admit I did see that she had a point. So I set off alone and not without apprehensions of my own.

I have never kept so close an eye on the rear of a car in all my fifty years of driving. But Pip Squeak drove beautifully. She was faultless. It was as if she wanted to make quite sure that I knew what a fool I was to trade her in for another. She really did drive well. But it was no use. The decision had been made.

So we drove to Sussex and Pip Squeak the second was waiting for me, all ready with a full tank of petrol. But there was more. They presented me with a huge bouquet of flowers and a bottle of whisky (Scottish, so the leprechaun wouldn't be interested, but I knew someone else who would). I was overwhelmed: such kindness, such generosity. How could anything ever go wrong again?

And yet nagging doubts remained. It was then that I had my brainwave. Before I did anything else I would go on a pilgrimage. The outward journey had taken me well across Sussex so now I cut south and west until I joined the A27 at

Pevensey. Another few miles west brought me to Polegate and soon afterwards I turned left onto an unclassified road through Wilmington.

Yes, you've guessed it. I had decided to pay my respects to the giant of Wilmington. Now I know locals call the giant 'The Long Man of Wilmington' but I've always had my doubts about that. I reckon that giant is a lady. Where did I get such an idea? Well I've read somewhere that no one knows for sure. And yet somewhere deep inside me there's something that says the giant is a lady. And if I feel that, it's probably something handed down in my family. After all, we have lived in Sussex for a very long time.

It seemed to me that if I was having to cope with a witch, it might be useful to draw on old family relationships and secure the help of the Wilmington giant or giantess. And I had decided to back my hunch. I parked Pip Squeak the second and took my huge bouquet of flowers and walked to the foot of the giantess. There I laid my bouquet reverently at her feet and asked for her help and support.

I went back to Pip Squeak feeling much happier and more secure. It had been a bit of a detour but I felt sure that it was worth it. Now I must head north to visit my brothers.

My road took me past Lewes and up to Haywards Heath, where the very first known members of my own branch of the family lived all those centuries ago. And it was there that I noticed the red light.

No, not traffic lights and not a pedestrian crossing. A red light *inside* the car on the dashboard. It couldn't be. It just wasn't possible.

But it was.

I pulled off the main road into a residential side road. I checked the owner's manual. It was all very clear and straightforward, yet I didn't seem to be able to find out what was wrong. Was anything wrong at all? I switched on the engine again and the little red light came on again.

91

So I took a careful note of *precisely* where I was and went to phone the RAC.

'Again?' said the telephonist. 'You haven't caught fire again?'

'No,' I said. 'I haven't caught fire again. I'm in a brand new vehicle, only collected today, and a little red warning light is showing.'

'Which little red warning light sir?'

'That's just the trouble,' I said. 'I can't make out which light it is.'

He sighed. 'Where are you sir?'

I told him *precisely* where I was.

'We'll be with you in about an hour sir. Just wait with your vehicle.'

So I settled down to wait. How fortunate I was that I was able to make myself a cup of coffee and generally look after myself. There are times when it really is helpful having a camper. Two hours later I rang the RAC again.

'Yes sir. He's on his way but he seems to be having some difficulty locating you.'

So again, I told the man precisely where I was and went back to wait. I decided to have a nap. The nice thing about a camper is that your bed is already there, so I stretched out and two hours later when I came to it really seemed to me as though the RAC ought to have arrived. I went back to the phone box.

'We are so sorry sir, we don't seem to be able to find you.'

'But I've given you my location twice.'

'Yes sir, but we can't find you. Two of our patrols have failed to find you.'

'But I'm in an old residential road off the A272.'

'Yes sir, so you said. But we can't find you.'

I was beginning to get the message. 'Have you got a map?' I said.

'It's on the screen in front of me sir.'

'Very well. Can you find the A272 as it comes into Haywards Heath from the east?'

'Yes sir.' my question might treat him like an idiot but he was determined to remain polite.

'Please take me through Haywards Heath on your map and name every turning off the A272 to the left.' I was being extraordinarily calm and patient you see.

So was he. He did just as I asked and then he suddenly stopped and said, 'There seems to be a bit of a gap in the map. Excuse me just a minute sir.' He brought the same map up on another telephonist's screen and found the same gap. He tried a third screen. 'That's funny sir. All our screens seem to have the same problem. I'll just fetch a Sussex atlas.'

I waited.

'I've got it sir. I shan't be a moment.'

There was a long pause. A very long pause. And then he said, 'That's strange. The page is missing.'

'Old Maud,' I said, thinking that I was saying it to myself.

'Pardon sir?'

I laughed mirthlessly. 'It's nothing. Just something I say when I feel like swearing.'

'Oh. Yes I suppose you must feel a bit frustrated sir.'

'Look,' I said. 'Ask one of your patrolmen to drive along the A272 through Haywards Heath from east to west. And ask him to check every single side road off to the left.'

'Yes sir. I'll do that sir, right away. If you like to wait by your vehicle sir.'

So I went back and made another cup of coffee.

An hour and forty minutes later the patrolman arrived. 'I'm afraid we've had a bit of a job finding you sir,' he said brightly.

I wasn't feeling too bright I'm afraid but it was pointless making a scene. So I waited until he asked, 'Now what seems to be the matter?'

So I told him and I showed him the red light. At least it still came on.

'This is a new vehicle sir.'

'Brand new. I only picked it up today.'

'So it's still under warranty.'

'Yes of course.'

'Then I'd better not touch it. I'll send a pickup truck.'

Suddenly my patience snapped. 'No,' I said.

'But that's all I can do sir. He'll take you wherever you want to go.'

'It has taken you five hours and forty minutes to find me. Do not *send* a pickup truck. *Fetch* one.'

'Well I don't know...'

'*Fetch one.*'

He took out his phone and rang headquarters. They authorised him to do as I asked and twenty minutes later he was back with the pickup truck and we set off on the long trip home. I never did get to see my brothers.

Damn that witch. She was clearly more than a match for my giantess.

We left Pip Squeak 2 at the garage with Jim, and the pickup driver took me home. He turned into the entrance to our lane and gasped.

'Do I have to take you down there?' he asked. 'It's so . . .'

I'm not sure what he was going to say but I spoke for him: 'Narrow,' I said 'Drop me off here, and thanks for all your help.'

I walked the last few hundred yards home wondering what on earth I was going to do about Old Maud. Damn her, she was not going to make me get rid of my rowan.

Wendy and Becky were both full of consolation. Nothing can raise the spirits of the depressed more quickly than the utter devotion of a dog and whatever it is that comes nearest to that from a wife. By the time Jim rang the following morning I was almost back to my normal happy self.

94

'Hello sir, your car's ready.'

'Oh good. What was wrong?'

'Nothing sir. It was just a faulty warning light, that's all. You can collect the car whenever you like. There'll be no charge of course.'

So that was that. We now had a faultless new car and thanks to the barometer it wasn't long before we had a chance to try her out properly.

The Barometer

I hardly know how to tell you about the barometer. Its story comes in so many little bits.

It was one September day when the wind had been whistling all around the hill. If it's really windy I can be sure that Wendy will either take me up onto the tops of the hills or else she will take me down to the sea to watch the breakers crashing on the shore, smashing on the pebbles and grinding them all forwards and backwards as the waves roll in and are then sucked back again.

We had all been down on the beach and were thoroughly exhausted from the power of the wind. We drove home and Wendy went straight down to the pond. She has taken to going down there every day after our afternoon walk. I can't see why she bothers. There's nothing but a few fish and half the time they're out of sight. Though they do seem to come up for her.

She scattered a sprinkling of fish food into the pond and the fish rose. So did her merman. He settled on the rock at the shallow end and she gazed at him.

'When are you going to get your barometer fixed?' he asked.

'Pardon?'

'When are you going to get your barometer fixed? We need proper warning of all these gales.'

'But how would the barometer help you? It's indoors.'

'That's no problem,' he said, but he didn't explain.

'If that's no problem,' said Wendy, 'why don't you watch the weather forecast on television? We do.'

He sniffed. 'Television is for humans,' he said. 'But real people and retired seamen use barometers.'

'Oh,' said Wendy.

'And yours is bust.'

'It's always been broken, ever since we first had it.'

'Well then, it's high time you got it fixed.'

When Wendy came back to the house I was settled comfortably in an armchair with a book and a coffee.

'Have you checked the answerphone?'

'Yes dear.'

'And when are we going to get the barometer fixed?'

'The barometer?' What on earth had put that into her head?

'Yes. You were so proud of it when you brought it home but it never worked did it? So when are you going to get it fixed?'

She was right. I was proud of it. It was old but more important than that, it was a beautiful piece of work. I'm not a man for antiques generally, not unless they really are handsome. This was.

It had been given to me by an elderly lady. I used to take her once or twice a week to visit an even older aunt of hers. The aunt was in a nursing home and the two women lived about ten miles from one another. It is amazing how many different ways you can find of travelling ten miles if you've a mind. I worked quite hard at making those journeys enjoyable and varied. When the old aunt died, my lady gave me the barometer as a thank you. My lady lived alone with her ginger cat. When her turn came to go into a nursing home she kept her house on just for the cat. Her neighbours loved her so much that they used to go in and clean and look after the cat. I reckon that must be about the only cat who ever owned a house without having to put up with sharing it with humans.

So I brought the barometer home and set it up in our porch. It looked just right. Oddly enough, it looked right just as it was, old and faded and not working. But it didn't look just right when we moved. We had just the right spot for it, that wasn't the problem. The problem was that in its new home in our hall it cried out for a spot of attention. It needed to be stained again, and it wanted to work. You could see it did. Yet Wendy had never mentioned it before. It was most irritating just as I was getting into my book.

'Well?' she said.

'Oh we'll get it fixed sometime.'

'When?'

And then I had a brainwave. Years ago I drove some American tourists who were staying in London. There were a number of places they wanted to go, not because they were interested but because they thought they should, and they liked being driven in the countryside. I must confess, I was surprised when they asked me to take them to Bristol. Bath, yes. Everyone asked to go to Bath, often taking in Salisbury and Stonehenge on the same day. But Bristol?

'We want to buy a barometer,' they said, and they showed me an article they had taken from an American tourist magazine.

'Are you sure you want to go to Bristol? I'm sure you could buy a barometer in London.'

'It's got to be antique,' they said.

'I'm sure you could get an antique barometer in London.'

'These people are specialists,' they said. 'They deal with nothing else.'

Who was I to argue? I took them to Bristol. They bought their barometer and haggled over the last few pounds and then paid me handsomely for taking them there. The journey made their barometer very expensive indeed.

But now I remembered that shop. Wendy's brother lives in Bristol. So when she pressed me to tell her when we would have our barometer fixed I said, 'The next time we go to Bristol to see Tony and Liz. There is a specialist barometer shop there.'

That could have been months away. I went back to my book. But Wendy went to the telephone. Minutes later she was back. 'Tony wants to know where the barometer shop is.'

I don't know. Never a moment's peace. I put my book down and went to the phone and told him. He knew the place but he couldn't picture the shop.

Trust Tony. I ought to have known. He went to have a look didn't he, and he found out about the shop didn't he, and it was gone wasn't it, so the question came again, 'What are you going to do about the barometer?'

I gave up. There would be no peace until I had sorted the problem out. I hunted through Yellow Pages and sure enough, there was a place not too far away that saw to barometers. So we drove there and Wendy was happy. I took the barometer into the shop and I believed that at last my troubles were over.

'I'm sorry sir, we don't deal with that kind of barometer.'

That kind of barometer? I didn't know there was more than one kind. I thought a barometer was a barometer and that was that. Apparently ours was an aneroid barometer, whatever that is.

'Do you know anyone who does?' I asked.

'There aren't many people about who deal with barometers at all,' he said.

I knew that was true. His was the only place in our Yellow Pages.

'There used to be a place in Bristol,' he said.

I could have crowned him but I kept my cool. 'It isn't there any longer.' I said.

'Well I don't know anywhere else I'm afraid. You could try London.'

I thanked him politely and returned to the car in despair. I didn't want to have to go to London but when Wendy has a bee in her bonnet she's like a dog with a bone. I knew she wouldn't let up until that barometer was fixed.

That night the phone rang. It was Liz, Tony's wife. 'Tony's been doing a bit of research,' she said. 'There's a place in North Devon that specialises in barometers.' She gave us the address and phone number and under pressure from Wendy I phoned the very next morning. After all, North Devon was a darned sight better than London.

Yes, they dealt with aneroid barometers. Yes, they would be glad to look at ours but they were very busy. It would take them about three months to get it done.

Early that December we took our barometer to North Devon.

A Trip to North Devon

I used to know that part of North Devon quite well. I did a lot of my growing up down there, although Wendy reckons I never did grow up. It was probably that plus a desire to try out our new camper that led me to suggest staying overnight. Normally we wouldn't think of camping so far into the winter. After all, ours is a very tiny camper. Staying overnight at that time of year was daft but I managed to persuade Wendy that we should.

We chugged across to Merton to 'Barometer World'. It's incredible. Merton is a small village right in the middle of nowhere between Okehampton and Great Torrington. And hidden away off the main road there is what is perhaps the best barometer museum in the country, perhaps in the world. It's amazing.

We took our aneroid barometer there and yes, they could certainly repair and renovate it. They told us how long it would take and they gave us a price...

I think perhaps I've given the impression that Wendy was very keen to have that barometer renovated. Suddenly her enthusiasm died a death when she heard what it would cost. But it was too late. By now I was thoroughly hooked. We wandered round the museum to give us time to consider the matter.

'We can't afford it,' she said. I ask you. When did that ever stop us doing anything? 'We really can't afford it. Don't forget that we've only our pensions to rely on now.'

She was absolutely right. We couldn't afford it. There was

101

absolutely no way we could afford it. I had to recognise the fact. When you become a pensioner your income is fixed. It has no elasticity. No, she was quite right. We couldn't afford it. So we asked the man at Barometer World to go ahead. And then we drove on to Hartland and parked for the night close to Hartland Point. The sun smiled on us and we walked along the cliffs and enjoyed the sight of the sea churning away at the rocks below. Supper and bed in our snug little camper, and then Maud's friends took over. They threw everything at us that night: rain, wind, hail, thunder, lightning, everything.

But our camper was facing into the wind and though she rocked pretty violently we were as snug as two little bugs. We even managed to get some sleep. By morning Maud's friends were so exhausted that they gave up and the sun came out again. We had breakfast, pulled down the roof, turned off the gas and set off for home.

'Are you going to show me something of Dartmoor on the way home?' Wendy asked.

Dartmoor? Why not? I know there are all sorts of strange tales about the things that can happen to you on Dartmoor and the presence of devils and suchlike, but I never gave these a thought. After all, the sun was shining. And anyway, we would be on the northern fringes of the moor. There isn't all that much access by road.

So we drove happily past Okehampton to the A30 and then turned off onto a series of narrow roads through Sticklepath and past Throwleigh and Murchington to Chagford. More of the same brought us down to the B3212 and to Moretonhampstead. We were beginning to feel peckish by now. We crossed the A382 and took to the unclassified roads again to Doccombe and Dunsford. Just outside Dunsford we stopped for lunch.

There's a place that overlooks the river Teign. It's a lovely spot and we were just lucky. Another week or two and they would have closed for the winter. Unfortunately dogs were not allowed, so Becky had to stay in the car. That always makes us hurry our lunch a little. We came back to the car and took her food and drink dishes out and put them in the car park. She wasn't very interested. She wanted a walk. So we set off for a walk in the woods, pushing her dishes under the car in case she was interested when we got back.

We were no sooner in the woods than Maud's friends struck again. The rain lashed down. We made that walk as short as we dared, fifteen to twenty minutes at most. And we were really racing when we got back to the car park.

Pip Squeak 2 wasn't there.

The two dog bowls stood in lonely state with the rain drowning Becky's food. She didn't seem to mind. She had found her appetite now so we had to wait while she finished her meal.

But Pip Squeak 2 wasn't there. It had taken a moment or two to register and then we hurried down to the restaurant and asked to use their phone. The police took all our details and promised to send someone. When he came the policeman asked to see where Pip Squeak had been parked.

I can show you the exact spot,' I laughed. 'There are two dog bowls marking the place.'

So we walked out to the car park. The two dog bowls weren't there. They simply weren't there. Now I can understand someone taking a car, but two dog bowls?

'Ah,' said the policeman, 'but this is Dartmoor idn it?' He seemed to think that this explained everything and then it was as if he realised that because we were grockles – tourists, visitors, incomers – we might not understand. He explained that the fact is that you can't explain. Not on Dartmoor you can't. Strange things happen on Dartmoor. We weren't all that interested. All we were interested in was how we were going to get home.

'Do you belong to any of the motoring organisations?' he asked.

'Yes, the RAC.'

'Then I should give them a ring.'

So we did. I gave the telephonist my name and membership number.

'Not you again.'

'Yes, I'm afraid so.'

'What is it this time? You've caught fire again? Or have you broken down ? Let me guess. You've run out of petrol.'

'Wrong,' I said triumphantly. 'Our car has been stolen.'

'Stolen? Who on earth would want to steal *your* car?'

''What did you say?'

'I'm sorry sir. I withdraw that last remark. What can we do for you?'

'We were rather hoping you could get us home.'

So they sent us a taxi.

We hadn't been home long when the phone rang. It was the police. 'We've found your car sir. It's in Exeter and it's quite unharmed except for the lock on the driver's door.'

'Oh wonderful. Thank you so much.'

'We were wondering how the thieves managed to start it.'

I had been afraid someone would ask that question. 'We left the spare keys in the glove compartment,' I said.

There was a long pause and then he said, 'I wouldn't do that again if I were you sir.'

'No.'

'And it might be an idea to buy yourself a steering wheel lock sir.'

'Yes I suppose it might.' Although, I thought, there would be a key to that with the spare keys.

He must have read my mind. 'And perhaps you'd like to consider fitting an immobiliser sir.'

'Aren't they terribly expensive?' And again I thought, 'and worked by a key with the spare keys'. Everything came down to those damn keys.

'Not too expensive sir. It's cheaper than having your car stolen.'

'Yes. Yes I see that. Do you think you'll catch the thieves?'

'I shouldn't think so sir. My guess is that some lads were out on the moor and got caught in the bad weather. Your vehicle' (he paused before he said 'vehicle' as if he didn't quite know how to describe it) 'your vehicle offered them a nice, easy way to get back to Exeter free of charge. But it may have been a group of lads who target car parks on the moor. If it is, we're more likely to catch them.'

Amazingly enough they did. The policeman told me what I had to do to collect my car so all was well that ended well.

The following February we had to travel across to North Devon again to fetch the barometer from Merton. It wasn't exactly camping weather so we decided to do the round trip in one day.

We were thrilled with the barometer. It really did look splendid. And it worked! It always makes you feel good when you bring something lovely back from the dead. And it looked just right in the hall.

While I was putting it up, Wendy went down to the pond for some reason or other. She's always going down to that pond.

'Hello,' she said.

'Hello lovely lady.'

'The barometer's back.'

'About time too.'

'Don't grumble. These things take time you know. Leslie's putting it up in the hall now. It looks fine and it works a treat.'

'That's good. Thank you for having it done.'

'I did it just for you, you know.'

'Yes I know,' he said modestly. 'Thanks a lot.' And with that he was gone.

Wendy came back indoors looking very pleased with herself. You'd think she had been off on a date with a new boyfriend or something. Her eyes were bright and she had that sort of smile which looks as though she is smiling inside as well as out. I assumed it was because I had put the barometer up. She certainly seemed pleased. I was pretty pleased myself. I'd been looking forward to being able to go to it every morning with a tap, tap, to check what it was reading and then to adjust it for the day. But Wendy always gets there first. It's so galling. She's the one who goes tap, tap and then she comes to tell me whether it's gone up or down. It's not fair. I wanted to be the one to go tap, tap.

Somewhat Sheepish

When the sheep are on the hill we don't go up there much. Sometimes it gets really crowded with several flocks and sheep everywhere. Not that we need to worry. Becky is well used to them and never gives them any trouble. She just plods quietly along with us until we're clear of them. She couldn't stay closer if we put her on the lead.

Once she probably saved a sheep's life. We were walking a set of fields we don't pass through very often. Goodness knows what I was thinking about. But I became aware of a sharp, single bark. It is the bark Becky gives when we have locked her out of doors and she wants to come in, a sort of pay attention bark. I heard it but I didn't pay much attention. I just wandered on along the path.

Again that sharp, single bark. I stopped and turned round. Where was she? And what did she want? Stupid dog. She barked again. I was a bit fed up at having to go back, but go back I did. There she was, standing in the field only a few yards above the path I had walked along.

'Come on,' I said, but she didn't move. 'For goodness sake come on!' I was getting really shirty with her by this time. But still she didn't move. I took her lead out of my pocket. That usually did the trick. When she sees that she comes slowly to within about a yard of us and then turns her head away just as we're about to put her collar on. She can be a real pain when she wants to. And she wanted to now. She didn't move, just barked once more.

I lost patience with her and strode over to put her on the

lead and tell her just what I thought of her. And it was then that I saw the sheep. The stupid thing had lain down in a gully in the grass, almost a sort of v-shaped valley, and it couldn't get up. When it saw me coming it tried, but it was stuck. I walked up topside of it, crouched down and got my hands under it as best I could, and then I heaved. Up it came onto its knees and its hind legs. From that position it was no problem for it to stand properly, shake itself and walk off with great dignity and not a word of thanks.

Becky's tail was going fifteen to the dozen. It's quite a bushy tail so you wouldn't expect her to manage nineteen. I felt so pleased with her and so proud, and also rather ashamed of myself, but she didn't hold it against me. She knows I'm thick. Anyway, after that little episode I reckoned that sheep would always be our friends and allies. But life doesn't always work that way does it?

There was one day when the sheep were on the hill, masses of them, and I decided to take Becky up there. We were no sooner through the gate than we came upon the first flock. They backed off and Becky and I climbed up past the 'Giant's Boot', towards the top. The 'Giant's Boot', by the way, is just a boot-shaped bit of rock sticking out of the hill. Strangely enough, although we gave them as wide a berth as we could, that flock followed us up the path. Sheep seem to do that sometimes, as if they think we know where the best grass is to be found.

Near the top we turned left. There's not much of a path but you can walk right round the rim of the hill in about three quarters of an hour (oh it's a big hill all right).

There were more sheep on the top but we didn't pay much attention to them. As we approached the second half of the heights beyond the leaning windswept blackthorn bushes, we saw by far the largest flock of all. They were scattered all over the hill top and all of them were staring at us – well, at me really. Becky had lagged way behind, which was unlike her. So

108

there I was with hundreds of sheep staring at me, and being joined by all the sheep we had left behind. They were also staring at me. There's nothing unusual about that. No? I'm not being conceited – well, not really. Sheep often do stare when people are passing.

Looking at them looking at me it did strike me that if I were a complete townie and didn't know better, it could be a bit spooky, all those big round eyes keeping you under observation.

I walked on quietly and looked at the view. After twenty yards or so I turned and looked back at the sheep. It was a bit like playing 'I see you'. I'd have sworn they were closer than they had been, and closer to one another too. But when I looked, they just stood still, staring.

I walked on a bit more and turned round suddenly. There was no movement, yet I swear they were closer still. And they were all looking at me with those big round eyes. I was beginning to feel a bit uncomfortable. It was almost as if I had cast a spell on them and they couldn't look anywhere else.

As if *I* had cast a spell? But then two ravens flew overhead. Oh no. Surely not. Old Maud wasn't at work again was she? 'Don't be daft,' I thought, and walked on again. But when I turned once more they really were too close for comfort. It was time to assert my authority. I stepped forward towards the nearest sheep.

She stamped her foot at me. It's funny the way they do that, stamp their foot and then turn and run. Only she didn't turn and run. She stamped her foot again and two or three of the others did the same. It really was quite funny. 'Get away!' I cried, and slapped my legs.

Ten of them stamped and for the first time I began to feel a wee bit anxious. But these were sheep for goodness sake. You can't let sheep worry you, can you?

And then they all stamped. Have you ever heard hundreds

of sheep stamp all at once? It was as if the hill shook. I certainly shook. Suddenly I was really scared. But what could I do? There was nowhere to go, no place to hide and no gate or fence anywhere nearer than half a mile away.

The lead sheep lowered its head as if it had horns. Thank goodness it hadn't. All the other sheep did the same and the whole mass of them began to move towards me, walking first of all and then beginning to run. I was rooted to the spot. I couldn't move.

Suddenly Becky began to bark at the top of her voice and run. She's not a collaborator for nothing. The collie in her surfaced now as she ran straight for the edge of the flock and began to turn it. Round the edge she ran and across the front of that mass of sheep. Their attention swung from me to her and the whole host began to turn.

But they were not turning to obey, they were turning to pursue. Imagine, sheep chasing a sheepdog. It was crazy. But I was safe for the moment. Clammy with perspiration I stood and watched anxiously. Becky now seemed to be in full flight with all those sheep going hell for leather after her. And then suddenly she stopped and turned and sank to the ground facing them. Oh no. She would be trampled to death. But! What! I couldn't believe my eyes. Right where she stopped a young fox leapt into the air, skipped, leapt sideways, flirted its tail and was off.

Once again the sheep were deflected. They ran as one mass after the fox and he loped ahead with a grin on his face. Was it a grin or is that just the way foxes look? Before long the fox stopped as Becky had done, turned and sank to the ground facing the sheep. And as it did so, another fox leapt into the air, skipped, leapt sideways, flirted its tail and was off.

By the time those sheep were back to me there had been five foxes. The last of them was right beside me, lying facing the sheep. The sheep were looking pretty done in by this time.

110

Becky rose to her feet. The five foxes did the same. They formed a complete circle round the sheep. For a moment or two there was a real stand-off and I wondered what was going to happen, but at least none of the sheep were looking at me any more.

At last the lead sheep stamped her foot, walked forward two paces and then turned and began grazing. In a moment or two all the sheep were busily eating away as if nothing had happened. I couldn't believe my eyes. Becky ran over to me with a self-satisfied smirk on her face as if to say, 'Silly man, scared of a lot of old sheep.'

I bent and stroked her to express my thanks and then I turned to thank the foxes. There wasn't a fox to be seen. I think they must have been the family we had watched growing up. They lived down at the bottom of the hill just below where we were standing. But why had they teamed up with Becky? After all, she always chases foxes, not that she ever gets anywhere near catching one. Perhaps it's all a game? I don't know. I shall never understand what goes on in other creatures' minds. I don't really understand what goes on in mine.

We set off for home and came across some parasol mushrooms so I picked a few. When we got home Wendy was just taking some washing in from the line.

'You've been a long time,' she said.

'Yes,' I answered. 'We were chased by the sheep up on the hill.'

There was a laugh from the kitchen and Joe came out with a mug of tea in his hand. 'You'll have to find a better excuse than that,' he said.

So I didn't bother to tell them what had happened. I just gave Wendy the mushrooms. After all, you don't want to make a fool of yourself too often do you? But I wonder if Old Maud did have anything to do with it. I wouldn't put it past her. She's a real pain in the neck that one.

Tall Trees Hill

It was in early summer that we had two visitors. Nobody we knew, you understand – just two ladies walking down the lane. I was out working in the garden. I do occasionally, though it seems a thorough waste of time when nature's garden stretches all around us in all directions. But there I was trimming one of the hedges when two ladies arrived. We chatted as people do.

'You must have a lovely view from your back garden.'

'Why don't you come in and have a look.'

We wandered around the garden and Wendy joined us. We both basked in the praises lavished on our garden and on our views.

'Oh look,' said one of them. 'Tall Trees hill.'

'Yes,' I said. 'Unmistakable isn't it? You can see it for miles around.'

'Yes you can see it. But how do you get to it? I've seen it so often and wanted to go there. And now I *must* go there. Can you tell me how to get there?'

I laughed because of course we go there all the time. It's one of our regular walks, especially when we're feeling particularly energetic.

'Yes, I can tell you how to get there. It's quite simple from here. But why *must* you go there? That's a very strong word to use.'

She hesitated and her friend, who had hardly spoken up to this point said, 'I think that is a question we would rather you didn't ask. Let's just say that going there is a kind of pilgrimage for us and we feel driven to go.'

How strange, I thought. 'Do you come from around these parts?'

'No but year after year we feel impelled to come back and every year we look at that hill and it draws us. This year its power has become unbearable. We *must go*.'

I took them out to the lane again. 'Just follow the lane,' I said, 'keeping the hill on your right.'

'On our right,' said the first lady. 'That's this side isn't it?'

'Yes, that's right,' I said. 'Right both ways. Keep right on until you come to a staggered crossroads. To your left is Hell Lane. Don't go to hell.' I do so love my little jokes. Little did I know how completely I was demonstrating my ignorance, but they didn't know either so that was all right.

'To your right, beside the staggered crossroads there's a farm gate. Go through the fields and you'll come to the foot of Tall Trees hill. A path leads to the top. It's all quite straightforward even if it is hard work. And part of the path is pretty muddy.' I looked at their shoes. 'I think, if I were you, I would go away and come back another day with proper walking boots or wellies,' I said.

'No,' they replied. 'Never mind our shoes. Now we're so close we must go on. Have you a trowel we could borrow?'

A trowel? What a strange request. 'Certainly,' I said, and off they went down the lane, brandishing my trowel in a right hand to remind them that that was their right-hand side.

It must have been all of two hours later that our front doorbell rang. Becky barked furiously as she always does and I opened the door. The two women stood there with my trowel. They looked utterly exhausted and their shoes were ruined. And yet their faces were shining and exultant . I have only seen such radiance before on the face of a mother with a newborn child.

'Thank you,' they said. 'It's done. We've left our offerings. Everything is going to be all right now.'

113

I hadn't the faintest idea what they were talking about. Wendy drifted into the hall.

'Would you like to come in for a wash and a cup of tea?' she asked.

'No. We mustn't stop. We've been far too long already. Our husbands will wonder where on earth we are. They're sitting in the car in the layby at the end of the lane. Thank you for all your help. We're so grateful and so happy. You just don't know.'

It was true, we didn't know. But we were glad to see them looking so pleased with themselves. They left and we found ourselves wondering what on earth had got into them. What had made it so essential that they go to Tall Trees hill? A kind of pilgrimage, they had called it. Did that mean that there was something about Tall Trees hill that we had never noticed? We had been up there often enough. Did it have some significance of which we were unaware? For instance: why were there trees on the top of the hill? It was a question we had never asked and we didn't know the answer. We had no idea. Why was it that those women *had* to go there? They were drawn to go there. They knew nothing except the old divine imperative. And having been, they knew that everything was going to be all right. We shall never know what drew them to that place or the dark secret which drove them on, if dark it was. There is a letter in my files. It came months after they had returned to their homes:

Thank you so much. We shall be back so maybe one day we'll inflict ourselves on you once more. We cannot tell you why we had to come but it is as we knew it would be after we had been there. Everything is all right now. There is a something about that hill, some mystique, some strange power for good and all is well with us. When we return it will be to give thanks, but we felt that we would like to write to say our thanks to you.

114

We had to accept that their mystery would remain a mystery to us and yet in part we understood. For there is something we have known ever since we came to this house, without ever understanding what it was. From the very beginning we have known that there was a rightness about this place which went far beyond anything we have experienced before. It goes way beyond the simple matter of being pleased with a house and buying it. Except for the troubles I have with Old Maud from time to time, everything in our lives is about as perfect as life can ever be.

But why?

What is it about this place and what is it about Tall Trees hill? It was a real mystery and it bugged me.

In the end I solved that mystery and several others with it, but it all took quite a while. And I wouldn't have managed it but for a few other strange experiences that year.

The Giant's Boot

Earlier that year, in the spring, Wendy had been strangely unsettled. I think she was missing the children. One day she said, 'You know we've been down here for nearly three years now and you've never taken me to see any of the sights.'

It was true. I'm not into that sort of thing. Great houses, monuments, museums, all leave me cold. Even splendid gardens rarely do anything for me. I'm much happier wandering our own hills and lanes. Besides, you can't take dogs to half of those places. What a good excuse!

'You can't take dogs to half of those places,' I said.

'What about the other half?'

So we began making monthly trips to see what we could see. It was late summer–early autumn before we went to Cerne Abbas to see the giant. I bought a book about him and read it over the next few days.

Seeing him and reading about him set me thinking about many things, especially the Long Man (or Woman) of Wilmington. I wondered why she (or he) hadn't protected me from Old Maud. Didn't she have the power? It was something which bothered me. And was she female or male? That bothered me too.

October began with some really lovely weather, almost like an extension of summer. It was on one of those lovely days that Becky and I made our way up onto the hill. Becky and the rabbits had a game of tag and I wandered on until I found a pleasant hollow to laze in. It never does to get home too quickly. Wendy feels that I haven't given the dog a proper walk. I stretched my waterproof out on the ground, lay down and watched the flocks of goldfinches moving from one patch of thistles to another. They chattered away to one another with their single notes.

Listening to them reminded me of my flute so I took it out and began to play. The turf all around me was close cropped by the sheep and the rabbits. There were still some patches of trefoil and a few flowers of the rough hawkbit, golden in the sun. 'Rough hawkbit', what a name. It deserves something better than that. Golden hawkbit? Goldilocks? Yellow sundial? I started trying out all sorts of names and repeating them more and more dreamily.

I never did come up with a decent name because my mind began to be distracted by other things. The hollow I was lying in was rather like a very small ancient Roman amphitheatre and it seemed to me as if the rising ground in front of me began to open up like the curtains on a stage. Two rooms came into view. One was a glorious banqueting hall with long polished tables covered in cut glass and silver. Throughout the hall there were fairies, pixies, elves and sprites all enjoying a magnificent feast. The high pitched chatter from the hall showed just how much they were enjoying themselves. They sounded rather like those flocks of goldfinches come to think of it.

I had put my flute away of course. And a good thing too. It would have clashed with the music from the other room. This was a ballroom complete with dance orchestra, polished floor and chandeliers. Up to a hundred couples were swirling round the floor, all dressed in the wonderful clothes of a bygone age. It reminded me of an old film of an eighteenth-century French court.

I lay back and looked at the sky. Three buzzards circled overhead. *Buzzards!* Oh heavens, surely my friends must be in danger. Should I do something? How could I warn them? I didn't want to spoil their feasting and dancing. Could the buzzards dive while I was lying there so near at hand? Did buzzards eat fairies? Did they even see them? I didn't. Well, not usually. I looked back at the two rooms. There were so many of the little people and they were all so happy. What on earth should I do?

While I dithered I hardly noticed that the sky seemed to be clouding over. And then, high above us came the buzzards' cries. At once there was a hurrying and a scurrying and a rushing and a shouting and a screaming: 'Close the curtains! Close the curtains!' At first I thought it was fear of the buzzards. As the hill began to close before my eyes I heard the most awful thumping like a succession of claps of thunder. I looked up at the darkening sky. I couldn't believe my eyes.

There above me were the two most enormous people I have ever seen. I recognised one of them straight away. He was massive and burly. I had seen him at Cerne Abbas. But who was the other one? I felt I ought to recognise her too. She was taller and slimmer. I racked my brains. I'd seen her somewhere. And then suddenly I remembered who she was. So I was right. Those stupid Sussex folk! There they were. They had taken all that trouble to make a memorial to the very last giantess in the land and then they had gone and forgotten that she was a lady. Fancy calling her the Long *Man*. I ask you. She was the one I had been to see when I collected the new car. And now, here she was in Dorset walking out with the giant from Cerne Abbas – there was never any doubt about *his* sex. The Dorset folk made quite sure of that.

Anyway, there they were standing on the hill with buzzards flying around their heads, mobbing them and distracting them from the panic of fairies down below. The giants were flapping at the buzzards the way we flap at wasps and flies. Suddenly I realised that the buzzards' cries had been a warning to the fairies, not a threat. Now they were keeping

118

the giants' attention while the hill was closed and the mansion lost to view.

At last, when the fairies were all safely out of sight, the buzzards circled higher and higher and then banked and glided effortlessly across the valley on the wind currents.

I was left looking up at the two giants who darkened the evening sky. I didn't realise how privileged I was. Here I was looking at the last two giants who ever walked the English countryside. There they were, standing hand in hand looking out to sea. The two of them were obviously courting. You could see that Hel, the chap from Cerne Abbas (for that was his name), was properly smitten.

These two giants were out for a stroll like any lovers anywhere. If they were in the habit of walking over our hill, it was no wonder that the top was such a mass of humps and hollows. The two giants were gazing out to sea. Hel pointed to Golden Cap. 'That's the highest cliff in the whole of the south of England,' he boomed.

'Go on with you,' she roared back. 'It's not as high as Beachy Head.'

'Oh yes it is. It's higher. Fancy a swim?'

'Yes,' she cried. 'Come on, I'll race you.'

She slipped off her sandals and tied them loosely together, hanging them over her neck and shoulder like a school satchel. Then she set off with great strides across the hill, down across the valley and up the other side towards Golden Cap.

Hel was wearing great heavy boots. As he clumped after her one of them got stuck in the side of the hill and came off. He hesitated, wondering whether to stop and put it back on, but she was getting further and further ahead of him. He didn't like being left behind so he ran on, one boot on and one boot off.

Up Golden Cap she ran and dived straight off in a beautiful swallow dive, straight into the sea with hardly a ripple. Up Golden Cap he ran after her, one boot on and one boot off, straight off the cliff in the most enormous jump. There was an almighty splash. There was nothing graceful about him.

The two of them swam out strongly and were joined by dolphins who came and swam all round them. For a time it was difficult to tell which was which. They were all diving, leaping out of the water, splashing and having the most wonderful time, though the chap from Cerne Abbas was the one doing most of the splashing, probably because he still had one boot on. Why on earth didn't he take it off?

'Race you to Portland,' cried the girl, and off she went with fine strong strokes, doing the crawl. The chap from Cerne Abbas set off after her. It was laughable – well, sad really. It reminded me of a time when Paul and Carolyne were young. They set off to swim from one side of a bay to the other. I turned to Wendy and said, 'Do you think I ought to go after them to make sure they're all right?'

'Perhaps,' she said doubtfully.

So off I went, swimming as hard as I could go to catch up. Only I didn't catch up. I got further and further behind and in the end they turned round and waited for me to make sure *I* was all right. It was so humiliating.

Just like me, the chap from Cerne Abbas fell further and further behind, and one of his legs felt like lead. He couldn't understand why.

The lady arrived at Portland and sat on the beach waiting for him. At last he arrived and clumped up to sit beside her, one foot hopping on the pebbles and one foot clumping in his boot. He dragged off his boot and hurled it into the sea in disgust.

'Why didn't you do that before?' she said.

'I never thought of it,' he answered sourly. He didn't like being beaten by a girl.

'Stupid fool,' she thought. 'I'm not marrying someone as

thick as that.' But she didn't tell him right out. 'I'm off home,' she said. 'See you again sometime perhaps.' With that she ran down to the sea again, swam around Portland and off towards the Isle of Wight. When she got to Cowes she found some ancient Phoenician merchant ships in the harbour. She pulled up a couple of tall fir trees, took one of the ships and rowed herself the rest of the way to Newhaven. There, she moored the ship but she took the two fir trees as souvenirs and walked home to Wilmington.

You can see those trees in the memorial carved to her on the hillside. She's holding one in each hand.

It's sad that she and Hel never married or had children. The race of giants died out in England when those two died. Mind you, their memorials really are something special. The tall lady of Wilmington stands two hundred and thirty feet tall. And as for the memorial to Hel at Cerne Abbas, why that's a marvellous erection!

Hell Lane

It was nearly November, so Wendy sent me down to the village to post a birthday card to Liz. As it happens I had just been reading some local history. You remember the great Civil War battle at Worcester in 1651? Of course you do. Prince Charles, who later became King Charles II, was defeated, escaped and hid in just about every old oak tree in the south of England. You *do* remember, you see.

After he hid in all those oak trees he came down to this part of the country to try to get a boat for France. He came in disguise with a few attendants to Charmouth and stayed at the Charmouth Arms. A Charmouth man called Stephen Limbry agreed to take Charles to France for £60. It was a risky venture but worth it if he could get away with it.

When Stephen Limbry's wife heard about it she locked her husband in his bedroom. She wasn't having her husband mixed up in anything so dangerous, not even for £60. So the boat never came for Charles. He rode on to Bridport and then turned back inland to Beaminster. As it happens, he moved on just in time. The Charmouth blacksmith had become suspicious of this group who had ridden their horses so hard. He examined their shoes and saw that the horses had been shod in different styles from different parts of the country. So he sent his ostler to report to the local magistrate.

The magistrate was also the vicar of Whitchurch Canonicorum. His name, like that of his more famous grandson, was John Wesley. When the ostler arrived in Whitchurch the vicar was in church and the ostler dared not interrupt him until he was free. The vicar promptly called out the local militia and rode to Charmouth. He called out the landlady, mistress Margaret, and asked about her guests. But he was too late. The bird had flown after planting a right royal kiss full on Mistress Margaret's lips. She wouldn't forget that in a hurry.

Some busybody told the parson about the kiss and he was scandalised. He told Mistress Margaret just what he thought of her and called down the wrath of God upon her head. But she wasn't scared of him. She stood her ground, hands on hips, She was careful not to let on that she had known who her visitor was, but she did make her sympathies pretty clear.

'If I thought it was the king,' she said, 'I would think better of my lips all the days of my life; and so you Mr Parson, get out of my house.'

All these things were buzzing about in my head as we walked down to the village. I posted the birthday card and then decided to take Becky on a long walk home. So we walked through the village and I pictured Charles and his friends riding through, followed some time afterwards by Mr Wesley and the local militia. I could see them riding hell for leather but all in vain.

Becky and I turned right off the main road and then after a while we turned right again and began the long climb up Hell Lane. I had often wondered why the lane was given that name. As we turned onto it, the weather suddenly changed. Strong winds and heavy rain soaked us through in moments and the clouds were dark and low.

The lane is pretty dark at the best of times, cut deep between two high faces of rock with overarching trees. Now it was almost like night. We slipped, slithered and squelched through the mud and a fast stream of water ran down the heart of the lane.

I say 'we' squelched through the mud. That's not true. Becky has the most amazing ability to find a way round mud.

She hates to get her paws dirty. So I was the one slithering and sliding up the hill – and what a steep hill it is. Perhaps I was beginning to understand the name of the lane after all.

I imagined someone at night, someone who had just heard Mr Wesley preach a blood and thunder sermon. Preachers were never very good at inspiring people with visions of heaven so they tried to terrify them into virtue. In my mind I heard old man Wesley ranting on about the wrath of God and the fires of hell with all the passion at his command. And now a solitary worshipper was on his way hone. He had spent the day visiting his parents in Whitchurch and now was on his way to his own home in Danesbury with no more than a flickering lantern to keep him company.

As he walked the weather broke as it had broken for me. With the storm all around him he began the dark journey along Hell Lane. Strands of ivy and bramble brushed against his face and scratched at him. A sheep coughed in the field beyond the trees. Fear grasped at his innermost being. He walked faster, struggling uphill through the clinging, cloying mud. He tripped over a fallen branch, stumbled in the ruts, tripped on fallen boulders, crashed to the ground, falling into the icy water. His lantern flew from his hand and went out. A fox screamed.

He also screamed. He struggled to his feet and began to try to run. He stumbled and fell again; stood and ran, stumbled and fell and all the time the ivy and the brambles brushing his face were playing havoc with his shattered nerves.

At last he reached the top of the lane and began to stumble down the other side – just as dark and muddy but somehow less fearsome if only because it was leading him home to the safety of his tiny thatched cottage. No wonder it was called Hell Lane.

So why did I question it? After all, here was I in the daytime and the lane was dark and cold and wet; steep and treacherous underfoot. And then there is that stream to contend with. Clambering up from the bottom to the staggered cross roads at the top, heaving my wet and weary frame up and up its steep climb, you would have thought that all questions about the name of the lane would vanish.

But they didn't. I remembered that Hell Lane has a very different aspect on a hot summer's day. Back in the summer I had stood in its cool shade with the dappled sunlight filtering through the canopy above, picking out the green of the ferns below. I had known what it was to stand in the peace and perfect tranquillity of that corridor beneath the trees and, with Becky, I had sipped water from the spring that never quite seemed to run dry – its water so fresh and clear, cool and pure.

How could anybody call it Hell Lane?

If only I had realised it, that spring of water should have begun to point me to the truth but I was still too ignorant to be able to make the right connections. So here I was faced with yet another mystery, the mystery of the name of Hell Lane.

Becky and I trekked slowly home, soaked to the skin. If only I could clear the quagmire from my mind as quickly as I could wash it from my body.

A Solution to the Mysteries

One winter's morning I sat in the conservatory. A heavy overnight frost had left everything white. The sun rose like a red ball behind the distant hills and then cloud turned it into a wide horizon of pinks, yellows, oranges, reds and greys.

In a field to the far left of me sheep were grazing and in the middle distance there were two more flocks in neighbouring fields.

Joe had taken the cattle in for the winter so the fields in front of us were empty. Empty? I knew the hedges would be full of birds. They always are. And there was a flock of gulls in the fields, mostly black-headed gulls in their winter plumage. A pair of them were a little apart from the rest. I knew them well. They have been around ever since we have been here.

We know them because they dance for one another. One does a kind of tap-dance on the ground, presumably to try to persuade worms and so on to rise to the surface and be eaten. The other gull watches for them to surface.

A fox sat near to the gulls, sunning himself. Was it the fox that made them nervy, or the pigeons feeding nearby? Every so often the pigeons were disturbed, flew off and settled a couple of hundred yards away. Each time the gulls followed suit.

One or two crows and a magpie sat on fence posts and watched. So did I. It isn't very often that I just sit doing nothing. But this once I just sat dreamily, taking it all in, loving it and letting my mind roam.

Had it only been the day before that Andy and Val and

126

their children had visited us? We had walked up on top of the hill enjoying the views across the sea to Start Point and Portland and the views across the valleys inland. Every hundred yards they are different. Andy asked, 'Are all these old earthworks the defences of an ancient hill fort?'

'No,' I answered. 'They're just the pits from quarrying for stone to build that village down there.'

So they were. The hill is covered with old quarry pits. But if I'd had an atom of sense I'd have realised that those pits were hiding an older secret and Andrew had pointed to it. They hide the fact that there was a settlement up there long before the village was built down below.

My trouble is that I'm too logical. You've noticed I expect. Yes, I always think in straight lines. Well, fairly straight anyway ... Oh all right, wiggly lines if you insist, but lines anyway. Yes, my thinking is linear. I've never been one for lateral thinking. I'm not even sure that I know what it means. But the way I see it is like this.

Imagine that a great fat spider came and sat in the middle of my sheet of paper. The body of the spider represents me ... Oh very funny. Thank you very much. Now imagine that I take each of the eight legs of the spider and stretch them out as far as they will go on the page. They are all pointing in different directions. Those represent my lateral thoughts, except that you couldn't really expect me to have eight thoughts all at once. But just suppose that I was thinking about the hill and the hill of the trees, and the giant and Hell Lane all at once. That's four lateral thoughts. Now let's go back to the paper. Suppose I take a pencil and draw a line around the tips of all the legs. I'd end up with a kind of circle. And suppose I do the same thing with all my lateral thoughts. The circle draws them all together into one whole.

As I sat in the conservatory that morning, that's exactly what I did and suddenly everything fell into place.

Do you remember the giant, the one from Cerne Abbas?

127

He was the key to unlocking all the mysteries. For he is not just any old giant. Oh no. Why do you think that there are only two ancient giants carved into our hillsides? It is because they are more than giants, that's why. Take the giant at Cerne Abbas for example. He's not just a giant. He's a god, one of the old gods from the earliest times. He's a warrior god, a protector, a hunter. He's the source of life and strength and virility and he's always closely associated with that other source of life: water. He was one of the supreme gods around these parts, perhaps *the* supreme god. I told you some time ago that his name was Hel (or Helis or Helith), but always Hel for short.

So there you have him: Hel the warrior, Hel the protector, Hel the source of life and strength and virility, Hel the god who is always associated with springs of water, running water, life-giving water.

Once you've grasped that, everything else becomes clear. Hell Lane isn't Hell Lane at all. All those Christian centuries with their talk of heaven and hell have led us astray. The lane is Hel's Lane and that poor, neglected spring causing a stream to run all the way down is Hel's magical, life-giving spring. No wonder the water tastes so cold and fresh and pure.

Now bring together the other two strands of my thinking. Hel's Lane leads up to two hills. One of them is what we call 'our' hill, the one I'd walked over with Andy. You remember that Andy led me to the conclusion that there had been an ancient settlement up there? Now I realised that some of Hel's people had lived up there, some of the ancient men, women and children of Dorset, the Durotriges. And what about the hill of the trees, the hill those two women went to see? Do you remember how they felt driven to go there, drawn to the hill? And do you remember their peace and radiance after they had been? That hill was Hel's sacred place.

There, all my mysteries were solved just by a little bit of lateral thinking. Evidence? Who needs evidence? There isn't a scrap of evidence as far as I know. But I saw the radiance on those women's faces. And we live in the heart of it all, between the home that was home to our distant forefathers and the hill that was their god's sanctuary. We live in the midst of it all, surrounded by the ghosts of the long, long distant past. There's an atmosphere of peace and harmony about this place – well there is as long as you can forget Old Maud, and she seems to have kept pretty quiet lately.

I was so excited. I ran through the house to the kitchen where Wendy was busy as usual. I poured out my new discoveries and she 'yes deared' in all the right places.

'Hel watches over us,' I cried. 'Hel's people watch over us and we are in our earthly heaven.'

And then the phone rang. It was Carolyne. Wonderful! I was all set for a long chat but she cut me short.

'Is mum there?'

'Yes, I'll fetch her.'

Off they went, chattering away. You know how it is when a mother and daughter start. I pretended not to be interested and stood listening behind the door.

'Is Leslie all right? He sounded ... I don't know, a bit ... excited.'

'Yes he is. He's just been off on one of his flights of fancy – only it's a bit worse than usual and much too complicated to talk about over the phone.'

'Oh dear. You don't think ... I mean ... I don't really know how to say this without sounding ... you know. You don't think it's time he was put away?'

Wendy roared with laughter. 'No, no, no,' she said and then paused. 'Well not yet anyway.'

It was a while after this that one of our neighbours said, 'I thought you might be interested in one of the lessons at the local school yesterday. It was about local history and the teacher told the children how "Hell Lane" got its name. Apparently there was a small community of Hellenes living around here centuries ago and the lane was named after them.'

Hellenes? Ancient Greeks? Now that *is* far-fetched – unless it's true of course.

Smugglers

Every so often Joe and Barbara have us over for a meal and every so often we have them over to us. One November morning Joe called in with an invitation from Barbara. It was in the middle of a period of really stormy weather. It had been stormy for weeks. There was nothing but wind and rain. First the wind would come whistling up from the sea. Then it would swing round to the east and blow across Joe's farm straight at us, and then it would come from the north and hurl itself down the valley. It really was rough and kept us stuck indoors much more than we like. So we were particularly glad to have Barbara's invitation to dinner.

And then the electricity failed.

'They won't want us to dinner now,' said Wendy. 'You'd better phone and put it off to another day.'

Meek and obedient as ever, I picked up the phone but that was dead too. The lines were down.

'Now what do I do?' I asked.

'You walk Becky across to the farm of course.'

So I dressed myself up and we set off across the fields. As we walked across Joe's yard the dogs in the barn began to bark like fury but when they saw it was only Becky and me they calmed down. I was so wet that I refused Barbara's invitation indoors and offer of coffee. I just passed on Wendy's message that we thought we ought to change our dinner date.

'Tell Wendy she needn't have worried,' Barbara said. 'I cook on the Rayburn.'

'And we've still got all the oil lamps we used to use when you came here as a boy,' said Joe, looking over her shoulder. 'It'll be just like old times.'

So we went. I drove right into the yard as close to the kitchen door as I could, and we ran in out of the rain.

It was an old, low kitchen warm from the range. The clothes airer hung empty from the ceiling just as it had when I first visited fifty odd years ago. And the long oak table and benches were the same. But the walls had modern cupboards and worktops and the old sink and the double drainer had gone. Now there was a modern sink, a dish washer, washing machine, fridge and chest freezer – all the usual mod cons and all of them useless without electricity.

The room was full of shadows cast by the two oil lamps, shadows of the past amongst so much that was new. The food was superb. Wendy was always glad to accept one of Barbara's invitations because she knew we would both enjoy it. She could enjoy a meal out anywhere but I like proper English food with no frills and none of that modern rubbish of plastering everything in herbs and spoiling the pure taste of good meat and vegetables. Joe was the same. So Barbara had cooked some of their own lamb with plenty of their own vegetables. And she followed it up with apple pie and lashings of clotted cream.

By the time coffee came we had moved to the lounge and were all full to bursting, warm inside and out and generally feeling good.

Joe said to Wendy, ''Tis no use asking him, but you'll have a brandy I expect?'

'Ooh yes please.'

'Have you always been teetotal Les?' asked Barbara.

'Yes I have. We were brought up that way. Joe was too. But people grew less rigid when we were in our teens. They probably had to. The war brought all sorts of changes didn't it? My family started to drink in a modest way. Even in their chapel society it slowly became the accepted thing to do. Funnily enough, I left religion behind and stopped going to chapel altogether, but I never acquired a taste for alcohol. And later, with drink-drive laws coming in, there didn't seem any point.'

Barbara swirled her brandy round the bottom of her balloon glass and laughed. 'You don't know what you're missing.'

'That's what I tell him,' said Wendy.

It was my turn to laugh. 'As long as I don't know, it doesn't matter does it?'

Joe poured a little more brandy into their glasses and looked out at the rain lashing down. 'It must have been like this back in they days,' he said. Typical Joe. Off he would go at a tangent. No one had a clue what he was talking about.

'Which days Joe?' asked Barbara gently.

'Oh,' he said, 'I was only thinking.'

'What were you thinking about.'

'Smugglers,' he said.

'Do you know any stories about smugglers Joe?' Wendy asked.

'Course I do. They were all about these parts. I was thinking of one particular time. The smugglers had an arrangement with the excise men and things had got pretty easy. They could even use the proper harbour as long as they came in by night. But then the excise men were changed. The smugglers let it be known that they would be landing one night as usual and when the signal came from the harbour that the excise men were there, they reckoned they had them properly fooled. But they were wrong. It was a filthy night that night.'

'Just like tonight by the sound of it,' I said.

The rain was lashing down and the wind was violent outside, and as we listened to Joe by the light of oil lamps we felt that we were right back in smuggling times.

'Ah,' he said and sipped his brandy before picking up the thread of his story. 'The smugglers hauled to about a mile out to sea where two whalers met them from out of our beach. They took off the brandy casks and began to row back to the beach while the smugglers sailed into harbour with nothing more than a catch of fish on board. The excise men checked them out but of course they found nothing. Back at our beach three miles away the bearers were waiting with their ponies. They loaded them up and began to wend their way up the valley inland towards your crossing up top of the hill. It was just mud tracks in them days.

None of them had seen the horseman sitting quietly up on the downs watching through his telescope. He signalled to another horseman, but that was where the smugglers got lucky. Because the night was so filthy, the second horseman didn't see the signal and eventually the first one had to ride over and pass on his message personally. That lost the excise men valuable time. By the time a troop of them had come up from the harbour, the smugglers were past.

'At the crossroads, well, crosslanes I suppose you'd call it, the smugglers divided up into three little groups. One came down here past our farm and ran smack into the excise men riding hell for leather the other way. Most of the men got away but they lost their ponies and their brandy. The officer in charge put an escort on what they had captured and sent it down to the harbour, and then he rode on with the rest of his men. At the crossroads he split up his men into two groups. One of them rode straight on but the smugglers had got safe to the Five Bells in the village. Underneath the window seat there was a deep hole where they hid their goods.'

'Where is the Five Bells?' I asked. 'I've never seen it.'

'No you haven't. It was burned down like so many places but it was a grand place for smuggling. And the smugglers used to ride on and bide a bit near the vicarage. It gived the impression that they had left their stuff at the church like so many did. Anyway, that night the excise men found nothing up that way. But the third group of them set off down your lane.'

'Our lane,' whispered Wendy.

'Oh yes. It was often used,' said Joe. 'Where it cuts between the steep sides you could hide a regiment of soldiers down there and never be seen, so a few ponies with brandy kegs was easy to pass through. But the men were uneasy that night. Don't ask me why. Instinct if you like. Something made them turn off the track onto the hill and lie up in a cave behind the gorse thickets up there. They waited and watched and sure enough, before long they saw horsemen riding hard down the lane. The excise men were after them. The smugglers watched them pass. Then they covered all the brandy with rocks. They could come back for that another day. So they dispersed and made their way safe home.

'But then the weather took a hand. It had been raining for weeks and the lake up on top of the hill was bursting its banks.'

'There isn't a lake on top of the hill,' I said.

'No more there isn't, but there was. That night it burst its banks and came pouring down over the hillside right past where your house is now. It brought masses of earth and rock down with it and completely covered that there cave with all the brandy in it. So that was lost for good. The smugglers came back for it but they couldn't never find it.'

'Don't you think you'd better go out and check the calves Joe?' said Barbara, bringing him back to the present.

'Ah. Yes, I'd better.' He swirled the last of his brandy round the bottom of his glass and drank up.

'Can I come too?' asked Wendy. 'I love to see them when they're so young.'

'Not so keen when they'm full grown I expect,' laughed Joe.

'Here, take my old coat and boots,' said Barbara, and off

135

the two of them went into the wind and the rain. When they got back they found the two of us settled either side of the fire. I had another coffee but Barbara had opted for a drop more brandy.

Joe pulled off his boots, hung up his coat and rain hat and Wendy did the same, talking excitedly about the calves. Joe looked at the two of us with our drinks and said, 'That looks a good idea. Another brandy Wendy?'

'Mm, please. It's a rather special brandy that one.'

I moved away from the fire a bit to make room for her and she snuggled up close. I may not drink brandy myself but I must say I like the way it affects her sometimes. We sat in companionable silence for a while.

'Did you have any bombing in the harbour during the war?' Wendy asked.

'It's funny you should ask that,' said Joe. 'Les came down here to escape the bombing in London and he used to come home here with me because it was so quiet and peaceful.'

'Well so it was,' I said.

'Mostly,' he said. 'Of course they bombers did come, they were only interested in the big places. We saw the fires sometimes and heard the noise. You could see the fires of Portland burning from here you know. But our little harbour was too small for them to bother with it much. I think they only attacked it when they were lost or scared. We didn't suffer much. But one night we had a landmine up on the hill above you.'

'Really?'

'Yes. Of course your houses weren't built then.'

'Whereabouts did it land?'

'Do you know the old boot about a third of the way up the path?'

'The giant's boot? The one the Cerne Abbas giant left behind?'

Joe looked at me a bit sharply. 'How did you know that?'

136

'Oh never you mind. You wouldn't believe me if I told you. Is that where the landmine landed?'

'Close,' said Joe. 'That boot used to be a lot deeper in the ground. But the landmine cleared a lot of the stuff over and around it and left a huge crater on the hillside. It's all grassed over now of course.'

'A good job it landed there where it couldn't do any damage.'

'It did kill a few sheep,' answered Joe. 'Dad was the first one up there. He was on Home Guard duty patrolling the hill. The first thing he saw was that old boot. He'd never seen anything more than a toe sticking out before and never realised it was a boot until that night. That was when he understood the old nursery rhyme.'

'What old nursery rhyme?' asked Wendy.

'You know the one:

> There was a young woman
> who lived in a boot,
> she had so many children
> all stuffed in the foot.
>
> Along came the squire
> from Down-a-Long Farm
> and rehoused the fam-ly,
> They came to no harm.
>
> He gave the young woman
> a job in his dairy
> and everyone called her
> Lucky Milking Mary.'

'Wasn't she an *old* woman?' asked Wendy.

'With all those children?' exclaimed Joe. 'She couldn't have been could she?'

She would certainly have *felt* old,' commented Barbara.

'I think I recognise the beginning of that, though it sounds all wrong somehow,' said Wendy, 'and I've never heard about the squire before.'

'Well you'm a townie idn ee. You can't be expected to know those old country poems proper can ee.'

I was enjoying this. Joe looked so serious and the more he pulled your leg the broader his accent became. But Wendy had had so much brandy that she didn't notice. She just felt rather confused. She was sure she knew the proper nursery rhyme but she couldn't for the life of her remember how it went.

I decided to pull Joe back on track.

'You were telling us where the landmine landed,' I said.

'Oh ... ah,' said Joe. 'So I was. Well dad found the crater and he scrambled down into it and had a look around. Good job he did too.'

'Why's that?' Wendy asked.

'There was something down there, that's why, and he covered it up quick. Then a couple of weeks later, when all the fuss died down and people had stopped coming to look at the crater, he went up there with his horse and cart.'

'What had he found?' I asked.

'Oh, you wouldn't be interested.'

'What do you mean, I wouldn't be interested? I *am* interested. Why d'you think I'm asking?'

'No,' he replied. 'It wasn't nothing that would interest you.'

He could be *so* irritating at times.

Wendy said, 'I think I know what it was.'

'Ah,' said Joe. 'You might too.'

Well of course, that made it even worse, and there was Barbara smiling knowingly into her glass. It looked as if I was the only one in the dark. I felt really niggled.

'For goodness sake,' I said, 'What's the great secret between you three?'

138

'Go on Wendy,' said Barbara, 'put the poor boy out of his misery.'

Wendy swirled her brandy round in her glass, took another sip and said, 'I think the secret's in the glass.'

'What on earth was she burbling about? I looked in her glass but I couldn't see anything and they roared with laughter.

'You're right at that,' said Joe.

'Your dad found the smugglers' brandy. The landmine brought it all to light,' said Wendy.

And as if on cue, at the word 'light' all the lights came on. The power cut was over.

A Nightmare

It's difficult being an ignoramus.

Bumping headlong into the other world, Old Maud's world, without any knowledge of it, I'm never quite sure which world I'm dealing with. Nor do I know when to keep my eyes open for trouble and when I can relax.

Take Christmas and New Year for example. Those times of year affect us but do they affect them? Do they reckon that those times of year give a chap like me so much trouble anyway that they don't need to give me any more? Do they call a truce?

It certainly began to seem like it. We actually had quite a pleasant Christmas as Christmases go. Some of the family came to see us. Everybody was happy. Nobody was sick. Oh, and I had my stock of handkerchieves and underpants replenished and nobody bought me a tie. What more could any man want?

New Year was just as good except that we were the ones who did the visiting. The trouble with that was that we went back to Surrey and to London and that brought on one of my nightmares. I haven't had a nightmare for ages. There was a time years ago when I had them pretty regularly but Wendy cured me of all that.

So why did London set me off again? I suppose it *was* London. It couldn't have been? No, surely not. Not up there. I mean, there haven't been witches up there for ages.

I think it was just being in London that set me off. Places do that sometimes don't they? There are one or two places that have a sort of haunting effect on me and London seems to have become one of them. Judging by the nightmare it does anyway. See what you think.

In the first place, I knew that I was having a nightmare. That seems strange for a start. It was one of the nightmares from my chauffeuring days, so I knew the way it would go. The details would be different but the end result would be the same. I knew all this but it didn't ease the tension or reduce the sense of panic.

I had to collect my solicitor customer. He was exceptionally demanding yet in one respect he was also one of the best customers I had. If he asked me to collect him at eleven o'clock outside his office, he would be there on the dot of eleven. In London that kind of customer deserves all the medals that are going.

For some strange reason Wendy was with me as I drove up to town. Why? She never came with me. It just wasn't the thing to do. Yet, as I drove the Jag quietly westwards along Fleet Street, there she was beside me. She had no business to be there. My solicitor would not be pleased.

Just before Chancery Lane, Fleet Street was closed off. It hadn't been closed two days earlier when I had driven my solicitor to his office opposite the Royal Courts of Justice.

Typical.

And I had timed my arrival to a nicety. It was no use trying detours. They would make me late. The only thing to do was to park the car, run around the blockade to the office and bring the solicitor back.

'Come on,' I cried.

Why did I take Wendy? It would have been quicker if I had left her in the car. We circled the blockade to find that a hotel had been built right across the road. It hadn't been there two days before. But this *was* London. Anything could happen in London. Should we run back a bit, cut down to the river and come up from there to the Strand? Or should we run up

Chancery Lane, round the back of the Courts of Justice and down again?

Neither. There wasn't time. We raced into the hotel but there seemed to be no way through to the back. We ran down a corridor and into a bedroom. A partition separated the room from the back half of the hotel. Wendy was onto the bed and over the partition in a flash. I stopped to take my shoes off before getting onto the bed. It's the sort of thing you do if you've been properly brought up. Oh dear. No, I'm not suggesting that Wendy wasn't properly brought up. I'm just ... oh never mind. Anyway, I took my shoes off and climbed over the partition.

Idiot! I had left my shoes behind. Back to the top of the partition. Two Chinese cleaners were in the room. Thank goodness. I pointed to my shoes.

'Could I have my shoes please?'

They looked at me quizzically. These strange Englishmen. One of them took off her shoes and offered them to me.

'No. Not *your* shoes. *My* shoes please.' I pointed again.

The other girl took off her shoes and offered them to me. I screamed, '*My* shoes *please!*'

A manageress came in. 'What's going on?'

I scrambled down, grabbed my shoes and fled, leaving the Chinese girls giggling delightedly. But we still couldn't get out. We were in a lounge overlooking gardens. The armchairs were full of elderly people as if the hotel were a nursing home.

'How do we get into the gardens?' I asked.

'You can't get out until you've paid.' The response was like a chorus.

'But we aren't staying here.'

'You can't get out until you've paid.'

I don't know how we did get out, but we did. We ran through the garden and on and on as if it were one of the avenues of trees in Bushy Park. And then we were on the

Strand and outside my customer's office. He had gone of course. It was ten minutes past eleven. He wouldn't wait ten minutes. He would probably never use me again.

Disconsolate, we walked down to the river. We weren't going through that hotel again. From the river we made our way back up to Fleet Street to the spot where we had left the car.

I knew what we would find before we got there. The only thing I didn't know was whether it had been stolen or towed away. It was always one or the other.

When I woke I wasn't sorry that our stay was over. We would be on our way back to Dorset later that day. Even Old Maud was easier to cope with than London.

Jasper's Discovery

Christmas and New Year were no sooner over than Wendy said, 'It's high time we had Barbara and Joe round for a meal.'

'Yes,' I said. What else could I say? And so another night-mare began. You know how it is I expect.

'What on earth shall I give them?' I didn't attempt to answer. I knew that whatever I suggested would be wrong and anyway she was just thinking aloud really. 'I can't give them beef or lamb or chicken,' she said. 'We'd never find a piece of meat that's a patch on theirs and I can hardly use any of the meat we've bought from them.

'Why not?' I asked. 'I'd have thought they would be pleased to know we can't do better than use their meat.'

'Don't be silly. They eat their own meat all the time. I could give them pork. They don't keep pigs.'

'Yes that would be nice.' I try to be encouraging, especially when I think it will bring these sort of questionings to a halt. But I ought to know better. She would go on worrying about it right up to the last moment, and when she did finally decide, she'd be quite sure that she had chosen the wrong option.

'I don't know. You do need to get pork absolutely right with nice crunchy crackling and the meat not too dry.'

'I don't know why you don't do a steak and mushroom pie. Joe loves steak and mushroom pie.'

'So do you,' she said. 'You're hopeless.' (I know. Everybody says so, so I must be.) 'You can't give people steak and mushroom pie when they come out to dinner specially. It's not the right kind of meal.'

144

'I don't see why not. I've seen Joe choose that kind of thing when he's been at a pub or a restaurant.'

'That's different.'

'I don't see that it is. If someone has special favourites they're the things to go for.'

'You just don't understand. And what about Barbara? I wonder if she'd like a nice piece of fresh salmon?'

I gave up and went out into the garden to do a bit of tidying up. I knew that the subject would keep cropping up until Joe and Barbara had been, so the sooner we got it over with the better. But what with one thing and another it wasn't until March that we had Joe and Barbara to dinner at our place.

I always keep well out of the way before these occasions. I'm more of a nuisance than a help so it's better to leave Wendy to it. One result is that I'm just as ignorant of the meal she has decided to give us as everyone else.

She began with some sort of fish starter which I didn't bother with. And then came the main course. She allowed me to carry in the vegetables. You should just see her vegetables. She does it every day, not just on special occasions. I don't think we ever have less than four or five different kinds and often it's seven or more. So I took in the vegetables and then sat down. That's what she had told me to do.

She brought in a pie. I was astonished. She cut it in a very unequal fashion. There were three fairly equal pieces and there was one huge helping. She gave Barbara one of the smaller helpings and asked her to help herself to vegetables. Then she gave Joe the huge helping and she and I had the other two. We were soon all tucking in and it was Joe who made the first comment.

'This steak and mushroom pie is delicious missus, really delicious.' Then he grinned and winked at me and asked innocently, 'Which supermarket did ee come from?'

'Joe!' exclaimed Barbara. She turned to Wendy, 'He's impossible. Don't you take no notice of him.'

145

Wendy smiled and said, 'If he can't tell the difference between home-made and supermarket he's not as much of a connoisseur as I thought.'

I took no part in this conversation, just enjoyed it. Besides, I couldn't get over the fact that Wendy had actually listened to me. Steak and mushroom pie! I knew it was right for tonight, and it really was. She makes a superb pie and this one was the tops. We all tucked in merrily.

Did you hear about young Jasper down the lane?' I asked.

'No. Who's Jasper?' Joe replied.

'You know who Jasper is,' said Barbara. 'He's the little boy belonging to that new family down the lane.'

'Oh yes, I know. They're not a *new* family.'

'You know what I mean,' said Barbara blushing.

'He means they're not incomers like us,' said Wendy. 'Don't worry. We know Joe too well to feel insulted. He loves to tease doesn't he?'

'He's terrible,' agreed Barbara. 'He makes me feel so embarrassed.'

Joe just grinned. He was completely unrepentant. 'What about this yer boy then?'

'You know,' said Barbara, 'it was in all the local papers.'

'I don't read the papers,' said Joe disdainfully.

'You don't read nothing,' she said, 'except farm prices.'

'So what's the story about this boy?'

'You tell him Les,' she said, so I did.

'His mother has been planting trees along the boundaries of their smallholding.'

'Yes,' said Joe, 'and she's had more sense than to plant a rowan by the roadside too.'

I ignored that.

'One day,' I continued, 'she was out there with her son. She planted a horse chestnut, turned round and Jasper was nowhere to be seen.

'"Jasper", she called.

146

'"I'm here," he answered.

'She could hear him perfectly clearly, but she couldn't see him.

'"Where?" she asked. "I can't see you."

'"I'm *here*," he answered firmly.

'But where was here? She looked all around her but he was nowhere in sight. Again she asked, "Where is here Jasper?"

'Now Jasper was only three and he didn't really know how to answer that question so he just replied, "I'm here. I'm here." And it was then that his mother noticed the hole. It was not one of the holes she had dug for her trees. She looked down the hole and there was Jasper standing on an old milk churn. She hauled him out and began to explore.'

'And I know what she found,' interrupted Joe. 'It was the old secret Home Guard headquarters.'

'If you'd read the newspapers you could have told the new family that. They didn't know what they'd found and they were asking,' said Barbara.

'If they were secret, how come you know about them Joe?' asked Wendy.

'My dad told me all about it after the war,' said Joe. 'He was in a special Home Guard unit. If they Jerries invaded, this unit was supposed to go underground and engage in guerrilla warfare behind the German lines.'

'I don't suppose they'd have lasted long,' I commented.

'No. Dad didn't neither. D'you remember when we was on exercises fighting for the Home Guard against the Yanks?'

I laughed and Wendy brought in a nice, light sweet which kept us all busy for a while.

'What was that about fighting the Americans?' asked Wendy.

''Twas part of their training for the invasion of Europe. They used to have mock battles with the Home Guard. They was always a bit of a farce really. The Home Guard never lasted five minutes.'

'But you were too young for the Home Guard,' Barbara said.

'We was in the Scouts and we acted as messenger boys. Only instead of carrying messages, we used to get ourselves captured as soon as we could.'

'Why on earth . . . ?'

'The Americans had chewing gum and baked beans and condensed milk and all sorts of other things we couldn't get. After the battles we used to go round all their dugouts and salvage all sorts of things. And they used to give us cigarettes and money too.'

'So the Home Guard always lost.'

'Well of course they did.'

'Sounds a bit like *Dad's Army* to me,' said Wendy.

'Part of the fun of that programme is that it isn't too far from the truth,' I said. 'It's a caricature, but a caricature has to be near enough to the truth or it isn't effective. Do you remember that time when your uncle's unit was being drilled?'

'Can't say as I do,' said Joe.

'Joe's uncle was a devout Methodist,' I told Wendy. 'And he was the platoon sergeant in the Home Guard. Their commander had been a major in the First World War. So, when he drilled his men he swore like the old trooper he was. Joe's uncle came smartly to attention and marched up to him and saluted.

'"Yes sergeant? What is it."

'"Zur," said Joe's uncle, "if you'm gwain to swear at us, us be gwain 'ome".'

'He was quite right,' said Joe, 'but not a lot of use if they Jerries had come.'

'No,' I replied. 'And I don't suppose a special unit down Jasper's hole would have lasted long either. I wonder if they've got tunnels there going to other places?'

'They'd have all fallen in by now,' answered Joe, and we dropped the subject.

But I quite often find myself thinking about that hole.

148

Ancient History

We moved through into the lounge and then I went and made the coffee. 'Do you know any other interesting things about the history of this area Joe?'

'What do ee mean? Things other than smugglers and the Home Guard?'

'Yes.'

'Yes I do. How far do you want me to go back?'

'How far is there to go back?

'I read once that there have been people round here for a hundred and fifty thousand years. I don't know about that but they've certainly been here since the last Ice Age and that's ten thousand years back.'

'What sort of people would have been here then?'

'Oh, just small family groups of hunter gatherers, living on roots and berries and shell fish and such. Mind you, by the time the Romans came there had been a whole series of immigrants and Britain was well populated and well organised into different tribal areas. Devon and Cornwall was the territory of the Dumnonii and Dorset belonged to the Durotriges. Their boundaries have hardly changed since those ancient times.

'Most of the time they just got on with their farming but they did a lot of fighting as well. They did love a good fight. They fought other tribes and they fought with one another. The old hill forts were centres of local power. And when they fought it was a bit like David and Goliath in the Old Testament. You remember that story I suppose?'

149

'Of course I do,' I said. 'It's a darned good story even if it wasn't true.'

'What do you mean? Oh I know. You mean David pinched the glory from the chap who really killed Goliath. What was he called?'

'Elthanan.'*

'Ah. Well I wasn't meaning that we should think about them. 'Tis the *style*, of battle that's similar. When two tribes or forces met one another, first of all they'd all shout at one another and blow horns and bang on shields and generally make as much noise as they could to put the frighteners on their enemies. And chiefs with chariots would ride in front of their enemies, charging up and down to show how brave and strong they was. And then the warrior heroes of both sides would fight one another one to one. And then last of all, everyone would join in, charging at one another, with as much noise as they could make. But all the time they would be looking over their shoulder to see if their friends was charging as fiercely as they was. And if they wasn't sometimes they would turn round and accuse one another of cowardice and start fighting against their own side.

'And even if they did all fight together, it usually wasn't long before one side took to their heels and went home. They would have some cuts and bruises to show for it all and a few would be more seriously injured or even lie dead on the battlefield, but 'twasn't usually more than that. It was a bit like cup final day really.'

'So when the Romans came they had to attack all the old hill forts,' I asked, 'places like Eggardon Hill and Lambert's castle?'

'And Maiden Castle at Dorchester,' added Wendy.

'Yes. Dorchester wasn't there then but Maiden Castle was

---

*2 Samuel 21, 19: 'and Elhanan the son of Ja-areorregim, the Bethlehemite, slew Goliath the Gittite, the shaft of whose spear was like a weaver's beam.'

the strongest hill fort of the lot. The Britons took masses of stones from Chesil beach up there to use in their slings when they were defending the castle. It really was a strong defensive place, but the Britons were no match for the Romans. They didn't have the organisation or the discipline.'

Wendy slipped out to the kitchen and opened the bottle of brandy that Joe had brought with him. She poured three glasses, brought them back in and settled comfortably beside me as Joe went on with his story.

'When the Romans invaded this country properly in AD 41, one of their generals was Vespasian. He commanded the second legion and he was the one who came down to this part of the country. He had ten thousand troops and they made fairly short work of storming Maiden Castle, although the fighting was pretty severe and a lot of people were killed. It took until AD 70 before the whole of this area was under Roman control. They had a tough job of it I can tell you.

'And that was when they built Dorchester, though they called it Durnovaria, and of course they built roads through the region too. They did a pretty good job I reckon and they kept control until about AD 400. By then their whole western empire was crumbling. But there's still remnants of their roads and villas and mosaic floors dotted about if you're interested. In fact they've discovered a couple more recently, one in Dorchester and one on a farm in Somerset.'

'I'm not that interested,' I said. 'Once you seen one of these things, that's enough for me. I'm not all that keen on visiting and looking at the things humans construct.'

'Idn you? Now that does surprise me. You like music and art and poetry. So why idn' you interested in buildings and mosaics?'

'Who knows? We all have our blind spots don't we? Do you remember our old English teacher? He loved art and literature but he had no interest in music, no ear for it at all.'

'Ah.'

151

'Joe, I think it's time we were going home,' said Barbara.

'You mean we're not going to hear about the Saxons?' I said with a grin.

She smiled back. 'Not tonight. Once Joe gets going he never knows when to stop.'

'They Saxons didn't have it all their own way,' said Joe, 'not down here they didn't.'

'Come on,' said Barbara. 'King Arthur can wait.'

'King Arthur!' I exclaimed. 'I suppose Joe will be telling us he's descended from Merlin next.'

'Perhaps he is,' she said with a laugh.

'Yes dear,' he said in a mock posh voice, 'I always was rather wizard wasn't I?'

'Get on with ee,' she said, and cuffed him round the head affectionately.

I think we all felt that we didn't want to wait too long before we dined together again.

Britons, Saxons and Vikings

Wendy wasn't a bit surprised at my selection of books from the library the week after Joe and Barbara had been to dinner. I took a small pile of them, all about King Arthur and the Saxon and Viking invasions. I couldn't bear to think that Joe might know more about this period of history than I did.

Besides, if he was going to start talking about King Arthur, who knows what rubbish he might come up with. There's so much legend and so little fact about Arthur. So I settled down to read.

One of the things I find hard about history is the difficulty of thinking back to other times. The face of the country has changed. Our attitudes to things have changed too. We go for a walk in the New Forest and love its beauty and peace. But our forefathers saw forests as dangerous places, places where there were wolves and wild boar. Read the fairy tales of the brothers Grimm. Listen to Badger's warnings in *The Wind in the Willows*. These show that the wild wood is a dangerous place.

Even William the Conqueror went round the Surrey forests rather than try to pierce through them. So one of the first things I noticed when I read about the coming of the Saxons was the fact that North and East Dorset were circled by the Coit Maur, the great forest. It was a real barrier to invaders moving west.

Another thing that is hard to visualise is the difference in population. The Saxon's didn't come in one great army and sweep through the country. A few ships arriving at the coast found it easy to drive the locals back inland. In many places it looks as though that's all they did. They drove the locals away and set up their own little communities. They did that at Lulworth and probably at lots of other places around the coast. Curiously enough, they called the locals the 'Welsh', which confirms the long-held view that there is a family relationship between the people of the West Country and the people of Wales.

Inland, when the Welsh or the Britons retired to their old strongholds on the hilltops, the Saxons left them there and settled in the valleys. There were battles of course and massacres, and that's where King Arthur comes in. He wasn't a king as we think of kings. He was just one of a number of British warrior chieftains, but he seems to have been one of the most successful.

The Saxons appear to have been trying to break through the Coit Maur into Dorset and the western counties. This was in the early 500s AD. But they met with stronger resistance than anything they had encountered further east. Did the Britons fight as the Romans had done or had they gone back to their old tribal ways of fighting? Who knows? But somehow they managed to organise themselves in considerable numbers.

There were a whole series of inconclusive battles ending with a great Saxon attack in about 516 or 518 on the fortified hill of Badon. It was a tremendous battle. Round about a thousand men were killed in it and the Britons under Arthur won a decisive victory. It was nearly a hundred and fifty years before the Saxons tried again.

But no one knows for sure where the hill of Badon was. All sorts of areas lay claim to it. It's good for tourism. It might have been Badbury rings between Wimborne and Blandford. Badbury rings looked down on two of the old Roman roads. Perhaps the Saxons advanced down the Roman road from Salisbury until they were stopped in their tracks.

We went to Badbury rings once – well, more than once actually, but it's the first visit I remember best. As you know, Wendy had bullied me into taking her on a monthly trip to see the sights around here – those sights where we could take Becky too. So we went to Badbury rings. Hill forts are nice, open places where a dog can really enjoy itself. Becky would love Badbury rings.

Wrong!

Dogs are forbidden: not just restricted to walking on a lead, actually forbidden. It's crazy. It's wrong. Dogs have just as much right to enjoy the countryside as humans and most of them do a darned sight less damage. But there it was. The notices were very clear. Dogs were banned. I was furious. We took Becky for a walk where she *was* allowed, in lovely open country round the foot of the rings. She and Wendy walked me off my feet. Even down there, the views eastwards were spectacular. When we arrived back at the car Wendy said, 'I want to go up to the top.'

'But we can't. Becky's not allowed.'

'Put her in the car. We shan't be long.'

'You go up. I'll stay with her.' I was still sulky because of those notices. And I was tired too.

'No. We haven't come all this way to see the rings only to go home without seeing them. What would Joe say if I told him? And you know how interested you are in King Arthur.'

I wasn't *that* interested, but it was no use arguing. I put Becky in the car and apologised to her.

'That's all right,' she said. 'I'm feeling quite tired as it happens so I'll just have a quiet snooze while you're away.'

Lucky dog!

Wendy and I climbed up to the rings and walked through the centre to look eastwards over that colossal view.

'Let's walk all round, Wendy said.

'*You* walk all round. I'll wait here. I'm done in,' I answered.

She was not very pleased. 'I don't know what's the matter

with you. Anybody'd think you were getting old. No stamina, that's your trouble.' And off she went.

She was right. I sank to the ground wearily and closed my eyes. All around me I could hear the murmur of the trees rustling in the wind. I heard the sound of men and the clatter of swords and clubs and spears and armour. The hill was covered in men, short, stocky, brown haired, all waiting. They seemed to be in some sort of irregular formation as if someone had tried to impose order and discipline without too much success. What were they waiting for?

I peered down to the Roman road below and saw a crowd of men coming down it. As they reached the foot of the hill they spread out and began to climb. One or two of the men on top of the hill took slings and tried to reach the men below with stones. A chap on horseback rode along the line of men telling them to hold their fire.

'Don't waste your shot. Wait until I give the order.'

The men weren't very pleased to be bossed about but they did as he told them. We began to hear the men down below shouting, teasing, taunting. 'Come on you cowards! What are you afraid of?' The taunting went on and on and the men on the hill grew restive. They began to shout back. 'Come on,' they said to one another, 'What are we waiting for?'

The horseman rode up and down the line. 'Wait. Wait. Wait. Curb your impatience. Don't listen to them. I'll give the order when the time is right. *Wait.*'

Still the taunts came from below as the men climbed ever higher and those on the top of the hill grew increasingly furious at being held back. One or two cooler heads joined the restraint.

'Do as he says. You know he always wins. He's fought these Saxons before. He knows how to deal with them.'

The hotheads went on grumbling.

'Fire your slings *now*! They are well within range!' shouted the rider.

They fired them off, stone after stone. There were shouts, cries from below, jeers from above but still the Saxons came on. The climb was hard work though. It took it out of them, left them puffed and weak-legged. Still Arthur held his forces back. He rode tirelessly up and down the line. 'Watch for my sword. When I swing it above my head, shout and go into the attack.'

He rode back to the spot beside me, a massive figure, fierce and commanding. Forward on the hill, three of his picked men watched the Saxons as the stones continued to rain down on them. One of them raised his hand, then the second and finally the third. They knew what their chief wanted and when he wanted the attack to begin. Arthur saw their hands raised, drew his sword and swung it above his head. 'Attack!' he roared. Over the top went his motley crowd of troops, brandishing whatever weapons they had – an occasional sword, clubs galore, a spear or two and here and there a scythe straight from the farm. They yelled, screamed their defiance and hurtled down the hill. Once moving there was no holding back – no possibility of holding back. Even the cowardly had to attack. The hill saw to that. They came violently on Saxons who were already sweating, panting with the exertion of the climb. They hurled them back down the hill and in no time the Saxons were fleeing in disarray. That one attack did it. It was all that was needed.

Jeers, taunts, cries of victory followed them as did some of their British enemies. Arthur and half a dozen more on horseback rode furiously through the Saxons, forward and back, slashing with their swords. It would be a while before those Saxons ventured to this area again.

It was. Most of Dorset, Devon and Cornwall remained British for another hundred and fifty years. And then the Saxons tried again.

'Are you going to lie there sleeping all day?'

'Sleeping!' I answered. I was insulted.

157

'Yes,' Wendy said. 'You were twitching and jumping just like Becky.'

'I was *not* sleeping,' I replied, now that I had come to properly. 'I was thinking.'

'Oh yes,' she said with an amused smile. 'And what were you thinking about?'

'About King Arthur if you must know. Did you know that he defeated the Saxons here sometime between AD 516 and 520.'

'Really,' she said.

'Yes really,' I answered as we set off back to the car. 'And it wasn't until about 665 that the Saxons attacked this hill again. But this time there was no King Arthur. They drove the Britons back here and they also attacked in the north of Dorset. They encircled the British troops and Dorset became part of the Saxon kingdom of Wessex.'

'And that's how it stayed until the Vikings came a hundred and twenty years later.' I knew a bit about the Vikings because there is an old tradition in my family that claims that we came over to Sussex with the Vikings from Denmark. Whether that's true or not, nobody knows. I was always a bit doubtful about it myself, but after reading about the coming of the Danes to this area, I began to wonder if the old family tradition might be true after all.

You see, the Danes came to these parts a number of times. Three of their ships came in 787 and there was the usual looting, raping and pillaging. They came twice more, in 831 and in 840. On one of those last two visits there was quite a battle fought where Charmouth is today. It was pretty inconclusive but the Danes never came to these parts after that. They went where the pickings were easier and richer.

But even from those three short visits they left their mark. In one of the villages round here they still call ginger-headed children 'Danes'.

And that was what set me wondering about my own family. There have been a fair few ginger-heads in my family, so perhaps we do derive from the Danes after all.

Young Maud

A few days later, after lunch, I was sitting in the conservatory watching a couple of wagtails on the garage roof cocking their long tails and picking up grit or insects. Down from them, in the garden, tits and finches visited the two feeding stations in a constant stream. Chaffinches, robins, a couple of dunnock (or should that be dunnocks? Hedge sparrows anyway) and a wren hopped in and out from under the hedges. One of the robins flew up into the sallow and chattered at all these intruders. A couple of blackbirds quartered the lawns and bathed at the bird-bath.

How lovely it all is. How relaxing and peaceful. It struck me that it was a long time since we had had any trouble from old Maud. Had she decided at long last to leave us in peace in spite of the rowan in the front garden?

Wendy came into the conservatory. 'Are you coming out this afternoon?'

'Yes of course.' I nearly always do.

We walked down the lane and took the second gate on the right into the fields. Halfway across a field below Tall Trees hill Wendy turned and saw a woman half walking, half running after us.

'I wonder what she wants,' she said.

'Who?' I turned and the woman also turned and danced off in the opposite direction.

'Strange woman,' said Wendy.

She was young, wearing a long black cape over black clothing and she had long, flowing black hair. Everything was

160

black except for her red wellington boots. I felt that it was Old Maud, but the age was wrong. I didn't say anything. Wendy had never met Old Maud so I didn't want to worry her.

We walked on and began to climb a steep path. Halfway up we stopped for a breather and turned to look at the view. The woman was there, running about all over the field.

'What on earth is the matter with her?' Wendy wondered.

'She certainly seems a bit odd doesn't she, not one of our usual hikers, that's for sure.'

We walked on to the gate. It is a new one and rather stiff. I managed to get it open and let Wendy and Becky through. Closing the gate was even more difficult than opening it. I glanced at the woman again. She reminded me of people I've seen in the old mental hospitals, walking in an odd, mannerish fashion yet with a hint of urgency about them as if they are in a hurry to get somewhere, and then rubbing their hands in an excited way. Perhaps she wasn't a witch after all. She was very young. Perhaps she had some kind of illness and her carers had lost her.

That was worrying. Ought we to do anything about her? I turned. Wendy and Becky were well up the lane, almost at the stile that was the beginning of our homeward trek. I hurried after them, slurping through the sticky mud that's almost always there on that stretch. As I climbed the stile I heard the bolt on the gate to the field behind us.

Should I say anything to Wendy? Should we do anything? I hurried to catch up and we walked along the hedge. Wendy looked back.

'She's come into this field too,' she said. 'Weird she is.'

'I won't look,' I said. 'Don't want to make her think we're staring at her.'

'Ooh. You must look. She's gone tearing across the field to the hills.'

I looked. It was true. She wasn't running in a straight line. She was haring about all over the place like a mad thing.

'Do you think she's all right?' asked Wendy. 'You don't think she's – well – disturbed do you?'

She certainly *looked* disturbed. But I didn't want to get involved. 'Who knows,' I said.

By now we were beginning to climb the main path onto the hill and we lost sight of her. We plodded along, stopping to look at the view over the sea. And every so often we used the view as an excuse to stop and get our breath back. And then, just as the woman was beginning to recede from our minds, she appeared on an outcrop immediately above us. She was looking down at us and I almost felt that she had willed us to look up at her.

She *was* young so she couldn't be Old Maud. She had a young face surrounded by that long, flowing black hair. She swirled her cape and ran away across the top of the hill. There she stood still on the opposite corner. She stood, like Nelson on his column, absolutely still, looking out at the view. Did she want us to follow? If she did, she was in for a disappointment. We continued our climb up the path until we came to the gates that divide the hill into two unequal halves. We passed through and then looked back. She was still there. I turned away to head for home but Wendy called me back again.

'Now look at her,' she said.

She was running round and round in a fairly large circle, her cape swirling in the wind. And then she stopped in one spot and twizzled round (three times I think). And then she was gone. Just like that.

'She's disappeared,' said Wendy.

'No.' She's only run down the hillside out of sight,' I answered. But I wasn't so sure.

We continued to look for a while but she didn't come back into view so we continued our walk home in peace.

Underground

The following morning, when Becky and I were on our own, I climbed the hill again and made my way to the spot where we last saw that strange young woman. There was a circle of soil that was completely bare. It looked as though the pasture had all been scoured away. How strange.

'Oh well. Here goes,' I thought.

Feeling a bit daft I ran round the bare patch in a circle and then I swizzled myself round in the centre, once, twice, three times. As you would expect, the ground opened beneath me and I fell. The last thing I heard was Becky barking. Strangely enough, as I fell I didn't feel the least little bit worried. All I could think of was Alice falling down into wonderland. But I had fallen out of my wonderland into the darkness below.

I landed on a thick bed of leaves. I was a bit shaken but quite unhurt. As I looked up the shaft I'd come down it was obvious that I would never manage to get up there again. And anyway, as I watched, it closed completely. Becky's face was the last thing I saw. I was in utter darkness and I sat still for a very long time.

Slowly my eyes grew accustomed to the dark and I realised that it was not quite as complete as I had thought. Ahead of me I made out a passageway just high enough for me to walk in. But it was still extremely gloomy and, as always when you're underground, there were creaks and groans all around that made me feel I wasn't altogether safe. The hill could collapse into the passageway and leave me trapped.

I don't know whether you've ever been underground? I

have. A few times. I've always found it a bit scary. The worst time was when a friend took me down a coal mine. I had a helmet of course, but he also made me wear knee guards. For a while I couldn't see the point of those. They call the lift in a colliery a cage and it goes down at a heck of a speed. I don't know how far below ground we were but it seemed an awful long way. We left the lift and found ourselves in a 'road' to the coal face.

It was cool and wide – easy walking, like a bridle path. A pit deputy came out of his cubby hole, checked us and walked with us a while, chatting to my friend. When he left us he grinned at me with a significance that was lost on me. The 'road' was so well constructed that the creaks and groans of the rock all around didn't trouble me much.

'When we open up a coal face,' said my friend, 'we build an entry road like this one to one end of the face and a similar exit tunnel at the other end. But when the face is almost exhausted, like the one we're going to, we stop maintaining the exit tunnel and it gradually folds in on itself. You'll see in a bit.'

Ahead of us there was a tremendous noise of machinery at work. 'Is that noise coming from the coal face?' I asked.

'Yes. You won't be able to hear a thing, but this shift stops in a minute or two and they'll shut it off. It's the trepanner, a machine for cutting the coal from the face.'

'So the miners don't actually cut the coal?'

'Only where the machine can't go. I'll show you in a mo'.'

We reached the coal face. The noise and the dust were awful. The great machine was carving out the coal onto a conveyor belt that ran right along the face and disappeared at the far end. Most of the men seemed to be doing little more than supervise and ensure that the coal was on the conveyor properly, but don't misunderstand me – it was hot, hard work. Some of the men were stripped to the waist.

And away in one corner, two men were cutting the coal out

by hand. This wasn't an area like the road, where you could stand erect. The men faced one another, kneeling on one knee and wielding picks with a sideways swing, each of them swinging in turn. Their muscular bodies glistened with sweat as they worked in rhythm with one another.

'That face is three foot six,' said my friend. 'In the old days we all worked like that right through the shift and some of the faces weren't much above two foot so we more or less had to lie down to get at them.'

I watched and tried to imagine. Get down under the kitchen table and swing a pick for eight hours in the gloom and dust and dirt, with the rock groaning all around you and the knowledge that men could be caught by flash floods, or by gas explosions or rock falls. It didn't bear thinking about. I had only been down there a few minutes but I couldn't have swung a pick like those two men even for that short time.

And then the machine stopped, though the conveyor belt continued. The men lay down on the conveyor belt and allowed it to take them from the face along the exit road back to the lift. My friend and I stayed a little longer. He showed me the trepanner in more detail now that it had stopped, explained the working of the mine and then told me to follow him.

'And keep your head down,' he cried.

He got onto the conveyor belt and I did the same – no easy thing when it was moving all the time. I lay flat, uneasy as we moved into the exit road. It wasn't a road anymore. It was just a small tunnel, big enough to carry the coal through from the face. And then the conveyor belt stopped!

Everything fell silent, except for the noise of the rock all around us, straining against the emptiness of the tunnel.

'What a nuisance,' said my friend calmly. 'They've obviously forgotten about us. We shall have to crawl, but we've only about another quarter of a mile to go.'

He began to move forward steadily, like a man swimming

the sidestroke, using an elbow and a knee. I did my best to follow and soon felt thankful for those knee guards. Every so often I rose too high and cracked my head on the roof of the tunnel. The sweat poured off me, but whether it was from the exertion or from fear I'm not too sure. I felt that the groaning and the creaking and the cracking of rocks would haunt me to my dying day. Just imagine *working* down here every day of your working life. It would be unbearable. No wonder most miners wanted their children to escape to some other form of work.

At last we could see light ahead and finally we were free to stand and stretch – a time for me to do my best to be nonchalant and to look as though I did this sort of thing without batting an eyelid. But I doubt I fooled anyone. We stepped into the cage and it took us quickly up the long ride to the top. The relief I felt as we stepped out into the daylight must have been obvious to everyone. And it was only afterwards that I began to wonder whether they had stopped that conveyor on purpose – to test me. The deputy certainly hadn't forgotten us. He was waiting for us at the cage. I don't know whether I passed their test or not. But privately I swore I would never go underground again. Yet now, here I was trying to feel my way along an underground passage again. Fortunately, although there were noises from the surrounding rock they were nothing like the creaking, cracking, groaning sounds I had heard down the pit.

My feet made no sound on the soft earth and the passage was so straight and so free from debris that my anxieties began to fade, particularly as there seemed to be a dim light ahead. But I had no sooner begun to welcome the light than I heard a voice. It had to be Maud – Old Maud? Young Maud? The thought of meeting either of them down here filled me with apprehension and a little shiver of fear ran through me. This was her territory and I was all alone without even Becky to help me. I crept forward towards the glimmerings of light until I was close enough to see that they were piercing into the darkness from the edges of a closed door. But I also saw something that gave me hope.

Just before the door my passageway came to an end at a sort of crossroads. I stood for a while and tried to get my bearings. It's almost impossible when you're underground, yet I was fairly confident. I felt that I had been walking south east towards the sea. If the path had continued I reckoned it would have brought me out somewhere between Eype and West Bay. After all, the passage had been straight all the way. Thinking along these lines I came to the conclusion that I had walked from what we call 'our' hill underneath the lane, back into the area below Tall Trees hill. I looked to the left of me.

There was a passageway that way but it had almost caved in. It looked as bad or worse than the exit road down the coal mine. There was no way I was going to attempt that passageway if I could avoid it. I guessed that it led out to Tall Trees hill. There was a spot there where an old building had collapsed and badgers had taken the area over for their earth.

To my right the passageway looked much better so I decided to give it a try. As I walked along it I thought about where it would take me and I began to think that my choice had been unwise to say the least. Fairly soon I came to a thick, solid door. It was locked and of course I knew who had the key. In fact I was pretty sure that if I could have opened that door, I would have come out somewhere near Old Maud's caravan. But since there was no exit that way I retraced my steps and took the passage which went more or less straight on from the passage I had been on originally. Unlike the other passages, it wasn't straight. It swung in a long curve round to the right and then came another disappointment. There was another solid, locked door and there was no way I could break through.

But where was I?

I stood for a while and tried to picture where I had been and where I had travelled to and then it dawned on me. This must be where Jasper's secret headquarters were. All those underground passageways must have been tunnelled out as escape routes or secret entrances so that the Germans would never discover where the Home Guard soldiers were hiding out. And perhaps where that light had come from there was a room which had been the officers' headquarters, their planning room. It was fascinating.

But of course, it didn't help me to get out. I tried shouting but no one came. There was only one thing for it. I would have to go back to that room and face the music. Once more I was overwhelmed with the knowledge that this time I was absolutely alone. So I retraced my steps with a great deal of foreboding.

Confrontation

As I retraced my steps and came to the underground door by the crossroads I heard a voice, saying in a sing-song sort of way,

> Oh cup of tea, dear cup of tea,
> he'll come to me, you'll see, you'll see,
> and when he comes he won't get free.
>
> He won't get free without the key,
> and where's that key?
> That key's on me.

And then she laughed a rhyming laugh, 'Hee, hee; hee, hee.'

When she had finished she started all over again. Funnily enough, as I listened, my fear passed and I wasn't unduly concerned. At least I knew where the keys were now. But I didn't want to be stuck down here for too long. Apart from anything else, Wendy would start to wonder where I was and I didn't want her to be worried unnecessarily. So I knocked firmly on the door.

'Come in,' she called. And then as I entered she added, 'I knew you would come. Couldn't resist it could you? Would you like a nice cup of tea?'

It was the young woman. I thought I'd better be as polite and friendly as possible.

'Hello,' I answered. 'Yes I would please. I wasn't sure whether it would be you or Old Maud.'

169

She laughed. 'Would you rather see Old Maud? It can easily be arranged.'

And there before my eyes she began to change. The long, shiny black hair grew grey and lost its sheen. Her smooth young face grew lined and wrinkled and her upright posture became bent. She seemed to shrivel and shrink before my eyes.

'Old Maud,' I whispered in astonishment.

'Old Maud it is,' she cackled. 'But I know what you men are like. You wouldn't have followed an *old* woman down here would you now? Oh no. She had to be young and beautiful. Sit down while I make us a nice cup of tea.'

Suddenly I wasn't so keen; besides I much prefer coffee to tea. I never drink tea at home as you know. But I sat down at the table and began to look around me. It was an amazing room. It was just like a bed-sitter with its own cooker, its own fireplace, a couple of armchairs and a small dining area, where I was sitting. On the other side of the room was a bed against the wall. At the end there was an open door which led into what looked like a prison cell. She saw me looking at it.

'That was for German prisoners of war caught by the Home Guard,' she said. 'I don't suppose you remember the Home Guard.'

'Yes I do. One of my brothers served in the Home Guard before he joined the RAF. And I served with the Home Guard when I was a Scout. I was a "runner" or messenger boy for them,'

'Oh! A real veteran then,' she mocked. She seemed to be taking a long time making that cup of tea. And she also seemed to me to be very careful to screen the cups from my view. That and her song made me more than a little suspicious. Surely she wasn't *that* predictable? She wasn't going to try the usual old witches' trick was she?

At last she turned and brought the cups to the table and

170

again I looked at her in astonishment for she had changed again. There she was, young, healthy, erect with those long tresses of shining black hair. She really was beautiful and she had such a soft, gentle, alluring voice.

'Here we are,' she said, 'a nice cup of tea.'

Just as she was about to sit down opposite me there was a bark outside the door. It was just one, sharp, single bark. I knew it at once.

'What was that?' she asked sharply.

'It sounded like my dog,' I answered.

'It couldn't be. You didn't bring your dog down here. There was no way you could have done.'

'No I didn't.'

The bark came again, just that one bark. That was Becky all right. She has always barked like that when we shut her out and she wants to come in.

'I don't know how she's found her way here,' I said, 'but it *is* my dog. I'd know that bark anywhere.'

Maud got up and went to the door. When she opened it, Becky barked away in the friendliest manner and jumped up again and again to tell her how pleased she was to have the door opened. She's like that.

Young Maud didn't like it. Some people don't. But at least, while she was coping with Becky's friendliness, I had the chance to switch cups. Then I called Becky off and made her lie down at my feet.

Maud came back to the table, gathered her wits, watched me sipping my tea and sat down. The dog had disturbed her quite considerably. She drank her tea down and pulled herself together.

'Nice place you've got down here,' I said.

'Oh yes,' she said. 'If ever I want a bit of peace and quiet' (she yawned) 'away from everybody and everything, I just come down here for a few days and relax.'

'It *is* very relaxing isn't it,' I answered and I yawned. Very

171

catching yawning isn't it? 'I don't suppose there are many people who know about this place.'

'No,' she said and yawned again. I joined her. 'No there's nobody knows.' Her voice was beginning to drift a bit as voices do when you're getting sleepy. 'Nobody knows but you and me and the badgers and. . .' Suddenly she sat bolt upright. 'What have you done?' she screamed. 'What have you done with the tea?' And then she flopped back in her chair and began to snore.

I waited a few moments until I was sure she was properly asleep and then I went round the table and began to hunt through her pockets. It didn't take me long to find her keys.

'You've saved my bacon this time and no mistake,' I told Becky.

She grinned. I'll swear she grinned. And then she said, 'Not just me. Me and my friends.'

'What friends?' I asked as I went to open the door – and there they were, sitting quietly in a heap outside, waiting.

Becky said, 'Allow me to introduce my friends. They were the ones who showed me how to get here: Mr and Mrs Badger and their three children.'

I bowed and thanked them. They grinned and waddled off along the small passageway. Becky and I took the other passageway to the door I had seen before. The largest key on the witch's keyring fitted. We left it in the lock and walked out into the morning sunshine. We were in the middle of Maud's wilderness by her caravan. If Wendy had been there, she would have wanted to look all around and see what the caravan was like. But I'm not curious that way. My only concern was how I was going to get out of the wilderness into the lane. I turned to tell Becky about my new problem but she had already gone. She can use the tracks made by wild animals, but I can't.

'Oh well,' I said to myself. 'If Maud's got an axe or something I'll just have to hack a way through. Unless I can learn to use one of these.' I put her besom between my legs and told it to fly but it took no notice so I put it back where I found it. I looked around but couldn't find anything to hack my way through so I went back down underground.

I locked the door and walked along the passageway past Old Maud's room. 'I wonder how long that drug will keep her asleep?' I thought as I crept past. Then I took the passageway to Jasper's secret Home Guard place. Another key on Old Maud's keyring fitted the door and sure enough I was through into Jasper's hidey-hole. But how was I to get out of there?

I made my way to the spot where Jasper fell in and shouted. In no time at all Becky had come to the hole and with her came Daz and Cob, Jasper's two dogs. Becky started to bark and so did Cob, but Daz just ran around all over the place getting very excited and squealing a bit. The fuss they were making brought Josie and Jasper across to see what was up. Well of course, nothing was *up*. I was *down*.

'Hello Leslie,' said Josie. 'What are you doing down there?'

'I've just been for a walk,' I said.

They took that answer in their stride and didn't ask any more questions. They knew it was the sort of thing I did. 'The trouble is,' I said, 'I can't get out."

'Oh,' said Josie. 'Never mind. Just wait there and I'll go and get my handbag.'

What had that got to do with anything? It was too late to ask. She and Jasper had both disappeared. The dogs had settled down just within my vision and were quietly waiting to see what happened, so I waited too. But I wasn't very patient. How much longer would Maud stay asleep? I was just about to start shouting for help again when Josie and Jasper returned. She was carrying a beautiful, shiny black handbag. She looked down the hole and turned to Jasper and said, 'I think it'll be long enough don't you?'

'Yes,' he said. 'I got out so I don't see why he shouldn't.'

Then Josie opened her handbag wide and Jasper put his hands in and slowly drew out an extending ladder. Honestly he did. It's quite remarkable the things ladies keep in their handbags. But I can't say I've ever heard of them carrying ladders about before. But there you are – Josie is a very exceptional young lady.

Jasper lowered the ladder down the hole and I climbed out. He drew the ladder back out and put it back into Josie's handbag.

'Do you want some eggs?' asked Josie as I tried to thank them.

It was lucky for me that she asked because the very last thing Wendy had said to me before I left home was, 'See if you can get some eggs while you're out. I need some for today's lunch.'

'Yes dear,' I had said obediently.

'Here's the money,' she had said. 'Now *don't forget* or there'll be no dinner for you today.'

'No dear. I won't forget.' But I had. I'd forgotten all about them. Thank goodness Josie asked me.

She and Jasper fetched half a dozen eggs for me and Josie took my money. I noticed that it went into her handbag and I wondered if that was all right, but I didn't say anything. After all, everything else seemed to be in there as well so perhaps it was right for her mummy's money to be in there.

Becky and I walked back up the lane and I gave Wendy the eggs. 'Well done,' she said in astonishment. 'You didn't forget then.'

'Of course I didn't forget,' I said. I was going to add, 'Do I ever?' but I thought better of it.

'Have you had a nice walk?' asked Wendy. 'I'm afraid we seem to have run out of coffee. Would you like a nice cup of tea for a change?'

'I think I'd rather have a dandelion and burdock,' I

answered. 'I'm off tea just at the moment.' And as I said it, I shuddered.

But she didn't notice. 'You're *always* off tea,' she said, and she laughed.

That was true enough. So I didn't have to tell her why I was especially off tea just at that moment. I'm glad of that. It's hardly the sort of story I could expect her to believe is it? And if she didn't believe me, she might start to wonder what really took me so long.

The Final Crisis

Have you ever sat and watched a herd of cattle? Yes, cattle. That's what I said. Have you? No, I don't suppose you have. Not just like that. Not to just sit and watch them and do nothing else. It was Wendy's mother who first taught us to do that. We used to put her out in the conservatory with her drink and her crossword but when we went out to join her we would find the crossword untouched, the newspaper unread. She was looking at the cattle. Endless entertainment they gave her.

I tended to be somewhat amused in the superior way that townies have when they're in the country. You know the sort of thing. I went to hear a speaker from London recently. He began his talk by telling us that it was a real pleasure for him to come into the country. It wasn't what he said that got to me, but his tone of voice. You'd have thought that we were a primitive tribe in the midst of darkest wherever and he was doing us a great honour by condescending to come amongst us. Pooh!

But I was guilty of the same kind of townie snobbery over those cattle. It wasn't until I started to sit out in the conservatory myself that I began to discover what fun cattle-watching can be. I often go out there now with my book and I begin to look at the views all around and focus on the crows and the rooks and ravens, or the rabbits or a fox. And then the cattle start.

I suppose it wasn't really until Joe came early in November and took them all away for the winter that we realised just how important they have become to us. As spring came round we found ourselves longing for their return, for we missed them terribly. And then May came and Joe brought them all back. We were thrilled. It was like welcoming long lost friends back home. We were absolutely delighted.

No, I'm not joking, I'm absolutely serious. You can mock if you like, but if you do you'll only be showing your own lack of experience and appreciation. We were townies too remember. It is so easy when you're a townie to lose the sheer delight and exhilaration that comes from watching other creatures go about their ordinary everyday lives.

It's true that in Surrey we used to watch the starlings come home to roost in their thousands and we used to wonder at the spectacle of those high precision flying displays. But have you ever watched a pigeon, or a rook or a crow or a seagull flying in the wind?

I sit in the conservatory and see them in their ones and twos flying down the valley in front of us. Sometimes, perhaps mostly, their flight is purposeful, a deliberate journey between two points. But often I swear that they're just flying for the sheer fun of it, swooping, diving, lifting on the air currents, free-falling, playing with one another. They have a marvellous time and they give us a marvellous time too. And that's what I mean about watching the cattle.

When Joe first brings them into the fields in May, they cling together and cling to one of the hedges or to the gate. All that space around them worries them. They huddle together for comfort. And then hunger begins to drive them further into the field and further from one another. At last it seems as though it suddenly dawns on one of them that all this space is theirs. She kicks up her heels and goes racing off like a mad thing. In no time at all others are doing the same, rushing about the field for no apparent reason at all.

It is rather like watching children who have spent a morning in a classroom and are now loose in the playground at last. They play games too, just like children. They play 'follow my leader', sometimes running and sometimes more sedately. They play 'let's have a stampede' when almost all of them go charging from one end of the field to the other and then stop and spread out for a chew of different cud. To us there is never any rhyme or reason to their antics, but there's great entertainment.

I said that 'almost' all of them have a stampede. Just like children, there are always one or two who won't play. They are probably the ones who get left behind when the main herd goes from one field to another. Much of the time it's Joe who moves them about. But there are times when he leaves the gates open and lets them wander where they will.

They don't spread themselves about in all the fields at once. They graze in one field and then they hold a meeting. All of them group together in a circle like spokes on a wheel. They press together towards the centre and have a chat. Afterwards they may disperse just where they are, or they may follow a leader like a school crocodile and file into another field. But there are always one or two who stay behind. At last they decide to go and join the rest, but as often as not they don't know which way to go. So they go to the fence and bellow. The anguish in their voices as they cry for help tears Wendy apart. She wants to rush down across the fields and show them the way to the gate. They bellow. Across the hedge their friends bellow. The noise is incredible. Eventually they find their way but it does take them a time.

One day when I was sitting out in the conservatory watching them, I had my sunglasses on because of the brightness of the day, and I saw Old Maud fly over. She circled round the field and at once the cattle moved together for one of their meetings. And then I saw Maud flying off towards the hill. There were sheep scattered everywhere over the hill, but soon after she had flown over I saw them all streaming down our side of the hill, lines of them all heading towards the lower stretches of the lane.

My attention switched back to the cattle. They had walked up to the gate Joe and I often lean on. It's a bit old is that gate. It isn't hung in any proper manner. Joe just lashes it up to the gateposts both sides with twine. It's perfectly adequate.

But it wasn't on this day. The cattle seemed determined to break through. Strong though that twine was, it wasn't long before it gave before them and the first of them were out in the lane.

I didn't know it, but the sheep from up the hill were in the lane too. They had found a spot where the foxes and the badgers go beneath the fence. It hadn't taken them long to make it larger and through they had streamed.

Thinking only of the cattle I told Wendy to phone Joe. Becky and I would go down the lane and drive them back. We hurried down the lane. They hadn't got far. Some were still only just crowding through the gate, and the sheep were beginning to infiltrate. The noise was incredible. Sheep on their own can be noisy enough. Cattle on their own can make an awful racket. But put both together and *all* of them together and you have never heard anything like it in your life.

But it didn't worry me. I strode towards them with Becky at my heels. 'Hoo, hoo,' I cried, and clapped my hands. That's all it needs. It gives a wonderful sense of power, striding up to these huge beasts and making them go where you want them to with just a 'hoo, hoo' and a clap of the hands.

They stopped. The lane was absolutely packed with animals. How they were going to manage to turn around I hadn't a clue. That was their problem though.

'Hoo, hoo,' I cried. But they didn't turn. They moved forwards, towards me. With all that noise they obviously hadn't heard.

'Hoo, hoo,' I cried and clapped my hands fiercely. They moved forward a little more.

'Hoo, hoo. Hoo, hoo.' There was a hint of anxiety in my

179

voice. I couldn't hide it and they sensed it. They moved forward again and I backed off a bit. It was then that Becky intervened. She ran forward and to and fro across the lane in front of them all, barking ferociously. That stopped them again. The heads of the cattle swung down menacingly. And then from Becky came a chattering series of barks such as I have never heard from any dog. For a moment or two the bellowing and the baaing dwindled.

'Come on,' said Becky, 'that'll give us a little bit of time but we must get a move on.'

'What do you mean?'

'Never mind your questions. I just asked them whether they thought the cattle should be first or the sheep. It'll take them a while to sort that one out. If we're quick we can handle them.'

'What do you mean? What are they doing?' I asked as we hurried back up towards our garden.

'It's Old Maud,' she said. 'She didn't like being tricked down in her lair. Now she's sent them to ruin your garden.'

'What!'

'Don't worry. All we need is your rowan.'

'My rowan?'

'Yes. Dig it up.'

'Dig it up? I'm not digging up my rowan.'

'Do you want everything in your garden eaten or demolished? Just do as I say and don't waste time.'

She can be quite bossy at times that dog. If she takes it into her head that she wants us to do something, she'll keep on until we obey. I fetched my spade, told my rowan how sad I was to have to do this, and began to dig.

Wendy came out. 'What on earth are you doing? You haven't turned those cattle back.'

'I know I haven't. I've tried but I can't. Is Joe coming?'

'They're not at home. I've left a message on their answerphone. Why are you digging up the rowan?'

180

'Becky insisted that I should.'

'Becky.' She looked at me as if I had lost it completely. 'Becky has told you to dig up a tree.'

''Yes,' I said, lifting the tree from the ground. 'Look, I don't understand this any more than you do but please, just go inside and don't interfere. Something has got into those cattle and sheep. I don't know what it is but Becky says the rowan will help.'

'You're mad,' said Wendy. 'I don't know what's got into you recently.' She stormed back into the house.

Becky had been sitting quietly on her haunches watching with considerable amusement. She had taken no part in our conversation at all. A more innocent seeming dog you never saw in your life.

Things were obviously hotting up down the lane. The cattle and sheep were in full cry again, and the birds and animals of the smallholding were adding their own chorus: cockerels, hens, turkeys, pigs, more sheep. It was an incredible cacophony.

I stood with my precious rowan in my hands. 'Now what do I do?' I asked.

'You're no good at climbing. Go and get your steps.'

'My steps?'

'Yes, and get a move on. They're on their way.' She bounded up onto the hedge just below the front gate. 'Hurry up,' she barked with some urgency. 'We haven't got much time.'

I fetched the steps.

'Put them up against your hedge,' she said, pointing with a paw. So I put them up against the hedge the other side of the gate. 'Now open the gate.'

'Open the gate? Are you mad?'

'Do as I say and don't waste time.'

'But they don't need the gate,' I said as I opened it. 'They can come in far more easily down the drive.'

181

'They won't, she said. 'Now. Take the rowan and climb up on the hedge.'

I was completely bemused by now but I did as I was told.

'Stretch the rowan across to me so that it makes an archway above the gate.'

As I did so, she took a branch in her teeth with great delicacy and placed it beneath her front paws. Then she straddled her body right across the branch and settled down so that it was kept firmly in place. We were only just in time. The noise from the lane was appalling. The cattle and sheep were jam packed into the lane and had almost reached our drive. But what struck me was the orderliness of their advance. They had answered Becky's question to them and answered it with incredible precision. I reckoned there were about fifty cattle belonging to Joe and about two hundred and fifty sheep from the hill. Now as I looked down the lane, to every one heifer there were five sheep all coming towards us in a noisy, orderly and determined fashion.

The first of them reached the drive and then stopped. I knew it. There was far more room for them to enter that way. It was pointless us standing where we were – not that I knew *why* we were. All I knew was that I had dug up my rowan for nothing – my poor, precious rowan.

The first great beast swung its head towards the drive and then away. It moved on up the lane with its escort of five sheep. It was as if something was drawing it. The firm determination faded from its eyes until you would almost have said that it was sleep walking, moving under some hypnotic compulsion. It gave one last great bellow and then passed through the gate under the archway of rowan.

I watched in astonishment as it moved slowly towards our front door, head and tail swinging in harmony, and then turned left. Its escort of sheep followed, all of them in silence. Down the path they went to the drive and then they turned and walked out of the drive and back into the lane –

182

down the lane. They had come in one gate and gone out of the other. I couldn't believe my eyes.

Out in the lane, those coming up were still making the most awful noise but as soon as they got to the gate and passed under the rowan they fell silent. Up they came, one group after the other, in at one gate and back out and off down the lane.

It was then that I remembered something I had read long ago. I don't know whether they still do it, but the old Scottish farmers used to make a large hoop of rowan branches and drive all their cattle through to protect them from disease, and then finally they would go through the hoop themselves. It was the rowan, my magical rowan. Oh I was so proud of it.

At long last I could see the last of the cattle and sheep coming up the lane. They were still bellowing and baaing furiously and behind them was Old Maud, driving them on and making almost as much noise as they were. Perhaps it was because she was making so much noise and was so intent on driving the sheep and cattle up and into our garden that she failed to notice the docile line coming back down the lane and past her. Nor did she seem to notice what was happening as they passed through our gate. She went on shouting and driving them on to the very last minute and then she passed underneath the rowan too.

The change that came over her had to be seen to be believed. It wasn't just that she fell silent as all the cattle and sheep had done. She began to change. I had seen these changes before but this time I had the feeling that I was seeing a change that would be permanent.

Old age fell away from her. She ceased to be an old hag with lank, grey hair and wrinkled face and became a young woman again. Her long, shining black hair framed a healthy country girl's face. The stoop of the old woman was gone too. She was upright and strong as she strode back down the lane.

Deep inside me I felt that this had been the last great crisis and that it was all over. *Old* Maud would never trouble us again, and I felt that Young Maud would be no trouble to us either. The conflict was over and we could live in proper neighbourly fashion as we did with everyone else in the lane. It was a wonderful feeling.

The Rowan

After the cattle and sheep and Maud had disappeared, Becky and I waited for a moment or two and then set off down the lane ourselves. Old Joe's cattle were spreading through the fields, placidly chewing the cud as if nothing had happened. I hoisted the gate and put it back. Then, using Joe's old twine, I tied it in place. I made a mental note to bring some new twine down one day and then continued on my way.

There was no sign of Maud. I didn't press my luck by nosing around the edges of the wilderness but went on down the lane to the place where the sheep had broken through. They were back on the hill, still filing their way up to the heights. I made some rough repairs to the fence and decided to phone the farmer and tell him there had been a break out. And then we went home.

Once home I picked up my spade. It was time to dig a hole and restore the rowan to its place. I heard a cough. Was it a cough? Or was it a bark? I looked at Becky. She was sitting watching me. She had been such a good dog. I don't know what I would have done without her. I wandered over to her and patted her on the head. I played with her ears and told her what a clever dog she was. 'Now I'd better get that rowan planted again or I shall lose it,' I said.

'Plant it behind the garage,' she said.

She stopped me in my tracks. I didn't expect her still to be talking. What am I saying? I've *never* expected to hear a dog talking.

'Behind the garage,' she said. 'That's the place for it. It'll do better there, and Maud will think you've got rid of it completely.'

'But I wanted it by the gate.'

'Don't be such an obstinate old fool,' she said. 'You know Wendy will be pleased.'

'How dare you call me an obstinate old fool.'

'Well you are,' she said. 'If you plant that tree back by the gate, it'll die. But plant it behind the garage and it'll do well' And then she added cunningly, 'especially if you give it plenty of well water for a while.'

Well water. Yes, it was high time I opened up my well again. And then Wendy came out again to see what was going on.

'Joe's cattle are back in their fields I see.' And then she noticed the rowan in my hands. 'You know,' she said, 'you're going to have to move that tree. It doesn't like it here in the front. It would be far happier down with the other trees behind the garage.'

What she meant was that *she* would be far happier with it down behind the garage with the other trees. But she was certainly right about it not being happy in the front. It hadn't done at all well and if I'm honest, I *had* been worrying about it. Now I had dug it up it was obvious that I must give way gracefully.

'You're quite right,' I said. 'That's just where I'm going to put it.'

'Wonders will never cease,' thought Wendy but she said no more than 'Oh good. I'm sure it will do well there.'

I fetched my spade and dug a hole for the rowan behind the garage. Then I took my key and opened up the well. I hadn't opened it for months. After all, the garden didn't need watering through the winter months and so far this spring there had been enough rain for all the garden's needs. Now however, I opened it up.

'Hello you lovely man.'

Oh gosh. She was still there and as beautiful as ever. I could

186

have wept for joy. I fetched the old bucket. 'Now where are we going,' the leprechaun asked. 'Not back to that nasty tasteless stuff you filled my bucket with last time.'

'Yes,' I said. 'I've got to give a tree a drink.'

'You've got to give a tree a drink. Mad. But then you're English aren't you. Give a tree a drink,' he said and laughed. He laughed until he cried, repeating over and over, 'Got to give a tree a drink. These English! What will they think of next?'

I gave the soil a good soaking, planted the rowan tree again and whispered my thanks for all she had done for us, and then I put my things away.

Looking after that tree gave me plenty of excuse for opening the well so I saw plenty of my nymph over the course of that summer. Perhaps that's why I never noticed how bright-eyed Wendy always was after she had been down to the pond.

But on that famous day it was good to be able to phone Joe and tell him that his cattle were safely back.

'Ah,' he said, 'Zo I zee. You'm getting to be almost useful now you been down yer for a bit. Us'll make ee half a countryman yet.'

Coming from Joe that was real praise. But I didn't really deserve it. 'I couldn't have managed without Becky,' I said.

'Ah. Well, thank you anyway. I'll 'ave to do something about thicky gate one day.'

'Yes,' I said. And then, 'Hang on a minute.'

Wendy was shouting from the kitchen. 'Invite them for a meal.'

What, *again*, I thought. You can have too much of a good thing can't you? But we *had* got something to celebrate. At least, I had and so had Becky, though we wouldn't be able to tell anyone. They wouldn't understand. Never mind.

'Wendy wants to know when you can cane to dinner,' I said.

'You fetch her to the phone and I'll fetch Barbara. They can sort that out. 'Tidn for us to make decisions like that.'

So that's what we did and in due course Barbara and Joe came to us again.

A Clean Town

The run up to Joe and Barbara's visit was remarkably easy. Wendy decided to cook roast beef and to use their beef. It's her favourite (I prefer lamb myself, or pork). I was so pleased to have her decide so easily that I gave her nothing but encouragement.

'I do hope the Yorkshire puddings will turn out all right.'

'Of course they will. They always do.'

That wasn't strictly true, but you know the sort of conversation. It all meant that when Joe and Barbara arrived, everything in the kitchen was going well and I was keeping carefully out of the way.

'What's happened to your rowan tree?' asked Barbara.

'What do ee mean?' said Joe in some surprise.

He hadn't noticed! All that fuss about my rowan and he hadn't noticed that I had moved it. I remember once that my dad grew a moustache. My mother and my sister nagged and nagged at him to shave it off. Eventually he did. Neither of them noticed either.

'I've replanted it in the back garden behind the garage,' I said, 'where Wendy and Joe thought I should.'

Becky ran across the room with her tail wagging. I bent down and played with her ears and added, 'Becky thought it would be best if I moved it so I did.'

I don't know why they should all find that amusing.

Then Joe said, 'Blimey. So you've seed sense at last. My gorr that wive of yours don't half have a lot of power over ee. But 'tis for the best. That poor old tree wouldn't never thrive where he was but ee will now.'

I hate to admit it but time has proved him right.

Barbara decided it was time to change the subject. 'You've been here quite a while now Wendy. Do you feel properly settled or do you find yourself wishing you were back where you came from?'

'No, I never feel that,' Wendy answered. 'Of course I miss seeing the children regularly but that's the only downside. We love it here. Everything is so fresh and beautiful. I love walking the hills and out to the cliffs or down on the beaches by the sea.'

'But what about the town? Don't you long for something bigger with more shops and theatres and things?'

'No,' she said. 'I'm not much of a one for shopping and I can find everything I want here. As for theatres and restaurants and such, you know, it's a funny thing ... She paused. 'Before we came here we used to go to the theatre a lot and eat out fairly often too. But now we just don't seem to want to go out of an evening at all. But if we did there's plenty going on, good quality stuff too – especially music.'

'So you idn gwain to be like a lot of grockles then?' queried Joe.

Wendy grinned. 'Go on,' she said.

'Well a lot of folks move down yer because 'tis so nice and quiet and then they finds they can't stand it, so they goes back where they came from.'

'No,' said Wendy. 'There's no fear of that. We're here to stay.'

'You feel the same way I'm sure Les?' It was Barbara enquiring in that kindly way of hers.

'Oh yes, I love it here. Mind you, I'd love it even more if there was a decent music shop in town where I could buy sheet music, but the library has plenty of music books to keep me happy.'

'Is that your only complaint?' asked Joe.

'Almost. I think they should pedestrianise the centre of the town.'

'What, the *whole* of it?' exclaimed Joe.

'Yes,' I said. 'It wouldn't be difficult. The car parks are all strategically placed and it wouldn't be hard to provide extra parking. There are no great distances involved. It would transform the town – especially on market days.'

'You won't be very popular if you suggests that,' said Joe.

'But he might be right,' said Barbara thoughtfully.

'There's no need to worry Joe. No local council has the courage to take that kind of decision without debating it for thirty years. And by then, they've so clogged up the outskirts that they can't provide the extra parking the scheme needs.'

'But you think 'tis a pretty decent sort of town on the whole?'

'Yes I do. It's such a pleasure sitting here at night looking down on it with its warm, orange lighting. It's unpretentious, solid, decent and clean.'

'You wouldn't have said that if you'd lived yer back in the eighteen hundreds,' he said.

Here we go, I thought. He'll be off on one of his history lectures in a minute.

Wendy asked, 'Why's that Joe?'

You'd have thought she would have learned not to encourage him.

''Twas a filthy place. The town was full of muck. The rivers was all polluted and cholera kept sweeping through the town. And of course, they had do-nothing councils in they days too. There was a parson tried to get things moving, a chap called J. Lettis Short. He spoke at meetings about how the town needed cleaning up. Lots of people came to his meetings but nothing happened. I think it was in 1849 that the government sent Dr Buchanan to look at things and he wrote a damning report, but still no one did nothing. And then a series of pamphlets came out written by folk calling themselves "Dr Cleanhouse, Dr Pureair, Professor Washwell and Professor Hateslop" but *still* nothing was done. In the end the government had to force the local authority to act. In 1870 Dr Buchanan came again and in 1872 a water company was set up and work began to improve the town's drainage.'

'So now we've got a lovely, healthy, clean town,' I said, thinking to draw this conversation to a close.

'Ah,' he said, 'but there is one little twist in the tail of this story that you might like to hear.'

We might, I thought, but then we might not. Ah well, he wouldn't rest until he had told us. So I said, 'And what's that then?'

'Well, you know how they used to beat the bounds of the parish?'

'Yes,' I said, 'they used to do it everywhere. Up in Hungerford the town boundary takes them in the door of a pub and out through a window – though I reckon most people pick up a pint on the way.'

'They've started beating the bounds here again haven't they?' said Wendy. 'I read about it in the *Thunderer.*'

'Gyaw,' said Joe admiringly, 'you *have* settled in if that's what you call the *News.* I thought it was only locals called it that.' And then he got back to his subject.

'Yes,' he said, 'they've started beating the bounds again. They used to do it every year in October and it meant crossing the millpond. Well, in 1891 there was all these do-nothing dignitaries, the mayor and his chaplain and all the corporation, all of them going round the boundaries with a host of people in tow. They came to the millpond and clambered onto the raft that would take them safely across to the other side. But you know how it is with dignitaries. They all wants the limelight. None of them wants to be left out. They all pushes and shoves to get to the front like women at a jumble sale. Well, they all got on the raft, all except the borough surveyor. He was left behind with all the crowd that was following the council. The raft shoved off and then it toppled over. All the councillors fell in and got soaked and the borough surveyor was nearly as soaked from the splashing.

'I've often wondered about thicky raft. Was there too many on it, or did someone tip it over on purpose? Anyway, I reckon it was a judgement. That's the sort of thing that should happen to all do-nothing councillors who fail to serve their town selflessly, faithfully and well. That's what I say.'

Through her laughter Wendy said, 'Come on Joe. You know as well as I do that being a councillor is a thankless task. It's often difficult to get enough people to put themselves forward.'

'Ah, and them as does puts themselves forward and more forward and more forward still,' he said.

'What's got into him tonight?' said Wendy.

Barbara laughed. 'He's just been refused planning permission for a new barn. That's what all this is about.'

'But I've no doubt he'll find a way round,' I said.

'Oh he'll find a way,' she said, 'always does.'

And he did, though it took a while. There's usually a way if you're imaginative enough. I remember once, when I lived in India, monkeys were becoming a real pest in the local hospital. They stole patients' food, they broke medical equipment and they terrorised the nursing staff. Believe you me, monkeys in the wild are not always the amusing chaps we watch in the zoo.

The medical superintendent applied for a gun licence 'to shoot the monkeys'. But there is a Hindu monkey god so he was refused. He applied again for a licence 'to shoot pests'. Again he was turned down for similar reasons. He applied again 'for personal protection'. This time the licence was granted. So you see, there's usually a way and Joe got his barn in the end.

And I've come to the end of my story with us living 'happily ever after' in our wonderland. We're in harmony with our neighbours (even Maud) and at peace with ourselves.

'How boring.' Is that what I hear you say? The truth is that we have never been less bored in our lives.